SILENT STRUGGLE

RESILIENCE THROUGH ADVERSITY

by

Spencer Bell

Featuring the short story

Welcome to Holland

by

Emily Perl Kingsley

Cover Illustration & Design by:
Alex Dickson

With thanks to Suzy Pope – thank you for your patience.

ISBN: 978-1-7385205-0-3

www.silentstruggle.co.uk

Thank you to Carolyn, Sam, and Aidan for all the love and light they have brought to my life.......You are my life. xx

To all the friends that have stuck with us.

"If you're going through hell, keep going"

Winston Churchill

West Bridgford is a beautiful suburb on the edge of Nottingham city. It's a middle-class heaven with many independent shops selling overpriced knick-knacks that nobody really needs and cafés selling the very best Jamaica Blue Mountain coffee and soya milk combos. It's for the strivers who want the postcode to send the precious children to the very best schools the city has to offer. It has a world class cricket ground, Nottingham Rugby, the world's oldest football club and is home to the back-to-back European champions Nottingham Forest. Its leafy and comfortable and you can even catch a tram into the city. It has a thriving nightlife and is bustling during the day with shoppers, moochers, and couples in tight athleisure wear enjoying the pavement café culture after their exploits on the trim trail.

Ben, Lou, Jake and Megan are proud to call Nottingham home but more importantly West Bridgford their home. The NG2 postcode really means something to those that know. Life is sweet and they are looking forward to a life surrounded by family and friends and growing old in this affluent part of Nottingham.

CONTENTS

Chapter 1

The Day That Changed Everything

Lou is heavily pregnant with twins. All is well and the family are preparing for a social gathering with their old school friends, school gate collective and some of Ben and Lou's family. It's Sunday and Ben and Lou are hosting. They have always been great hosts and there is pressure to ensure the event holds up, as expectations are always high. Even though Lou is heavily pregnant and expecting the babies anytime soon, she has been planning and preparing for weeks to get this event just right. The school circuit is a cut-throat one and there is a clear pecking order. Vying to be top dog is a huge deal and being the perfect host comes with massive pressure. Hosting a big thing is an opportunity to show off with the latest purchase from Oliver Bonas or by leaving out the 'right' brochure from The Conran shop, Sub Zero or John Lewis in an appropriately positioned spot on the worktop or coffee table. This is the elite group of parents and children, it's incredibly cliquey and if you don't know then you just don't know! It's all pretty stereo typical high achieving kids and parents – huge pressure.

The gathering of the great and good from school were

indulging themselves telling all within ear shot about their amazing careers, financial position in life, the next holiday to Watergate Bay boutique hotel and cherry picking their children's achievements to get their child to the top of the rankings for something.......anything. It's completely exhausting for Lou who tended to play down the children's achievements, whereas Ben never stopped talking about them in a way that would wind Lou up terribly. She prefers kindness and thoughtfulness over all else but lost the battle amongst a barrage of bragging from the assembled gathering. With twins on the way, Lou is heavily pregnant. She is hot, uncomfortable, and ready to sit down and get these twins out. It's a warm day and pretty sticky which adds to her discomfort.

As they discuss the future for their respective families and Ben and Louise talk of their latest plans for the house, Ben's pending promotion to partner and their expectations and plans for the twins. Most of the friends and family are swanning around with a glass of Moet getting steadily tiddly, rather than helping Lou deliver the canapés and keep people topped up. Lou relies on the usual four friends who always muck in, the most unaffected by their self-certified upper middle-class status. Lou has a lot of time for Victoria, Kate, Joy, and Fran. The rest are too busy swanning around in their latest White Company dress and diamonds. Swallowing as much champagne as they can and peacocking around the garden. Vicky, Kate, Joy, and Fran tended to just get on with things whilst the rest of the group just watched, not wanting to get hummus on their latest Victoria Beckham dress or drip chilli dip, tarnishing their Cartier watch. It was a running joke with the "Famous 5" who ran most of the get-togethers; preparing, serving, and clearing. They always had a good time together, laughing about the rest of the gang who spent most of their time looking in the mirror or finding the last sunny part of the garden to catch the evening light in their Versace sunglasses. Newbie couples are easy to spot as they work the garden and get pissed extra quickly, necking the Moet. One poor new mum to the group ends up in the flower bed having caught her new Jimmy Choo's in the lawn while tottering around the garden. Another dad trying to keep up with the hard-core drinkers ends up laughing, coughing, and puking into his cupped hands, much to the amusement of the West Bridgford Friday night drinking club.

It's still before midnight but, as the kids start to flag, the tiddly parents file off in awaiting taxis, lifts or ignore the fact they have had a couple too many and jump in the car and drive anyway with their kids.

Lou surveys the garden, spotting lipstick-stained champagne glasses perched on every available flat surface with the dregs of the Moet. Bamboo plates are strewn around with half-eaten canapes and the odd discarded Katherine Hammett pashmina left on the back of the garden chairs. She sighs and turns inside to ensure the kids are safely in bed. The garden will have to wait. She checks the kids and returns to the kitchen.

Ben's catching a cheeky cigarette outside as he has a big presentation the next day. He wants to get to bed as early as possible to catch the 6.10am train from Grantham to London. He takes a drag, silently praying that Lou gets through the day without giving birth until he gets back. It's a big day and is key to get the move up and, crucially, the extra cash. Ben takes a cheeky swig as they clear the empty bottles of champagne off the worktop and takes a final bite from the half-eaten canapes silver platters. Loading the dishwasher, they talk over the night and laugh about some of the conversations they had, Victoria making fun of Joy's Californian accent and Fran going on and on about her children, Tanisha mistaking the dog treats for a meaty dip tray and Verity coming onto some of the teenage boys flashing her thigh tattoos. They laughed about how pissed some of the guests were already and ready for the next set of stories to unfold.

They continue laughing about the guest's behaviour as Ben helps Lou up the stairs and whilst brushing their teeth, spluttering toothpaste over the mirror as they laugh.

Lou plods slowly across the bedroom and finally gets to sit down on the bed. She hinges her body, lifting her legs up and wrestles her bump to get into a comfortable position to try and get a good night's rest, knowing the garden needs tackling in the morning. Ben and Lou are glad of the early night – they are knackered. As they continue chuckling, they both gently drift off to sleep.

Ben is woken by a low, guttural noise coming from Louise. Opening his bleary eyes, he sees it's 1.00am.

'You ok, babe?'

'No Ben something doesn't feel right.'

'I am in real pain Ben.'

'Trapped wind again?'

'Ben! No, stop this isn't funny, it feels different, really painful. Stabbing pain really low down.'

'What do you want me to do?'

'We need to go.'

'I'll call 999.'

'No, Ben. Let's just go now, just get me in. This doesn't feel right. I'm not waiting'.

Ben helps Lou put something over her nightwear and gently inches her up to sitting position on the edge of the bed. Trapping his mobile between his ear and shoulder, he calls Terri, their neighbour, while searching out Lou's birthing bag. Ben needs to contact Terri to babysit Megan and Jake overnight and get them up for school until they get back with the twins. Ben wakes up Megan and Jake and explains they have to leave with Terri. As Lou is helped downstairs by Ben, she is crouched over in incredible pain and grimacing, whilst shouting back at Megan and Jake with a barrage of instructions about school, making no real sense. Megan and Jake just stand there rubbing their eyes in bewilderment. Ben leaves Lou leaning on the stair bannisters and grabs his food stash for hospital, and their coats, quietly anticipating the joy of the twins arriving into the world to complete the family.

Ben assists Lou, manoeuvring her towards the car and

shoehorning her in, reclining the seat back and springing the seat backwards to try and get comfortable. Now almost vertical, Lou grips the door handle and centre console, grimacing. Ben peers through the window screen, still slightly pissed but sobering by the minute.

They race through the dark streets of Nottingham centre to the local maternity ward, just 16 minutes away. Ben's eyes are everywhere – checking Lou, what's ahead, speedometer and every red light, bloody speed cameras and speed limit change in the city. Lou clenches her teeth at every turn, her eyes wide and hair sleeked down with sweat. The tension in the car is palpable. All Ben can do is reassure her as he speeds through the night.

Ben swerves the car onto the double yellow lines. Grabbing the bags and opening the door, he prizes Lou out of the seat. As they walk to the hospital doors all is locked so they buzz the night buzzer. Lou, whose waters have broken, is hunched over, leaning on the wall at the side of the door with one hand on the door frame and the other on her tum.

Peering through the window, they can clearly see a flustered midwife running towards them. As the door buzzes and opens, Ben blearily eyed explains.

'she's in labour and is struggling'.

Lou snaps back 'She!'

'Sorry, this is Lou she is my wife and is in real pain and needs to see Dr Vaughan'.

The midwife explains 'Dr Vaughan only works day shifts in the week, did you want a wheelchair'?

Lou wincing through the pain hurriedly says 'yes please I need cannot walk.

The midwife looks around the porch entrance and in the wheelchair park and there are none in sight 'Sorry it doesn't look like there are any chairs I can get someone to get one for you.

Lou hunched over in pain just looks down looking down raises her head up and through her straggly hair reluctantly looks at the nursed and with authority says, 'I will walk, Christ sake Ben!'

As they walk down the corridor, fluorescent tubes flicker away as the life drains out of them. The tired, sterile, magnolia-coloured, corridors are all quiet with the exception of a cleaner with a mop and bucket swirling her mop around the lino floor, avoiding the lifted corners. As they turn into the maternity suite, the atmosphere changes, resembling ER. Staff rush from room to room and the nursing stations are deserted. Ben looks down the main throughfare with doors – some open, some shut – running off the main corridor. The few staff that are there look stressed – hands on their heads and not a smile to be seen. Not quite the calm, welcoming atmosphere the pair were expecting.

They are led down to Room 3 by the first midwife they encounter. Ben looks at her name badge and notes it reads 'Helen Smith' Ben lets Lou know as he is crap remembering names, Lou just looks up at Ben despairingly. As they walk down, they can hear mothers squealing and wailing at various stages of birth. Bips, blips, buzzers are ringing out. Already in pain, Lou looks at Ben concerned, but Ben's face just mirrors Lou's concern.

They are both thinking *Where is the team that was promised to safely to deliver the twins?* Where the flashing lights, sirens, alerts, and team that were discussed. There thoughts synchronise both sure they are being led to a team and special room. They are both now pumped with adrenalin, worry and nervous anticipation.

As they are led into Room 3, the midwife then introduces herself as Helen Smith and explains that she is hours over her finish time and will not be with them long as there is a shift handover. Helen looks exhausted and flustered as she explains this is her first full shift after completing her training.

At 1.38am, they enter Room 3, Helen, and Ben manhandle Lou onto the bed. Helen wires Lou up to a CTG machine and various other sensors. Lous winces in pain.

'How's your pain from 1-10, 1 being slight pain and 10 being extreme pain?' Helen asks.

'Feels like an 8-9,' Lou replies through gritted teeth.

'OK let's get you wired up to a TEN's machine – let's start at level 3.'

'What's a TEN's machine?' Lou enquires.

'Its technical name is a transcutaneous electrical nerve stimulation; it's used mainly for back pain. It pushes electrical currents through your nerves to decrease pain. My father in-law uses it for his back when he gets a pain. It's pretty good'

'OK, we're connected,' Helen says,

Helen offers Lou Entonox, gesturing to Ben to watch as she shows how to suck on the pipe.

'Suck on this later if you feel any pain, but not to use it until we tell you to do so,' Helen says.

Ben and Lou are then left in the room alone as Helen has to go to other women in labour before signing off and heading home. Ben unpacks his snack box and ferrets through the birthing bag and Lou's snacks. Lou, neck pressed into her chest, grips the bed sheets with white knuckles and is shallow breathing through the wincing. She's had two children before, but neither birth felt anything like this.

Alone in the room, Ben and Lou feel incredibly vulnerable and isolated. A little time passes, and Ben starts to feel the effects of the champagne and, regressing into hangover mode, he opens up a box of snacks and sits there chewing on Rice Crispies Marshmallow Squares and a scotch egg, swigging water to fight off the pending headache.

Lou looks across. Wincing, snarling, and scowling she says, 'Christ Ben, really! A bloody bed picnic?'

'Sorry Lou, but I'm starving and feeling like shit.'

Locked away in a room with beeping, blips and the Cardiotocography (CTG) going off in the corner, digital numbers go up and down on the screen and paper is slowly spewing out of the front. Lou tries to breathe through the pain but reaches for the Entonox and sucks deeply on the mouthpiece. Ben, still scoffing his face, stares around the white lab-like room and at the powder blue curtains and lino floor.

'Can I put the TV on, Lou?' he asks.

A few moments pass. Ben delves into the birthing bag and pulls out his marmite sandwiches, munching through his and Lou's snack box while scrolling on his phone. Ben starts videoing Lou wincing in pain who snaps at him to 'quit that Ben'. Ben starts filming the room with his mobile phone panning around the room being mindful not to catch Lou in bed, he then takes a few selfies and posts them smiling and hurriedly scrolling and frantically pressing buttons getting them posted on Instagram.

After a while Ben says, 'How are you feeling now, is the pain any better?'

'No. Press the buzzer things don't feel right. I need to push'.

The CTG is intermittently stopping and there are temporary pauses in the bips and bleeps.

They wait a few minutes for someone to arrive. Nothing.

'Ben presses the buzzer again – now please!' Lou shouts.

A new midwife, Dorothy Warbouys, pushes open the door with Helen in tow. She surveys the room, mum, and the equipment with a steely stare. Dorothy's eyes are wide open, furtively analysing the key indicators. Using all her many years of experience Dorothy is calm as to not appear panicked.

Dorothy asks in a firm but measured way as to not put the fear of God into mum and dad.

'How are you feeling?'

'In pain, a lot of pain.' Lou winces.

'OK, OK!'

The CTG has stopped working and there are gaps in the familiar sounds of the heart monitoring device...Ba...Bum... Ba...Bum and then nothing. Dorothy wanted a consistent heartbeat and knew instinctively that there should never be any gaps when monitoring unless the twins hearts had stopped beating altogether. The gently pulsing, like listening to a heartbeat through a doctor's stethoscope is inconsistent and patchy. Dorothy knows that these gaps are bad as they could miss vital signals from the twins in mum's tum. Dorothy moves over to mum and adjusts the CTG sensor on Lou's tummy to get the sensor in position again to pick up the twins vital signs. Dorothy glares at the CTG monitor looking for a consistent line across the squared graph paper. The rises and falls are there on the screen, but the line drops off to zero, Dorothy moves closer and stands over the monitor, lifts up her puts on reading glasses draped around neck to take a closer look. Dorothy scans the CTG, pulling the paper out in front of the machine to assess the movements of the ink on paper. The graph should look like a mountain range on the horizon, but this one looks like its dropped off below sea level.

As Dorothy's eyes scan the paper, she looks up.

'Have you brought your birthing plan?' she asks with a hint of worry in her voice, turning the TEN's machine up to the max.

'Yes, it's in the bag,' Ben says.

'Helen, have you read the birthing plan?' Dorothy turns to the other midwife.

'No, I haven't!'

'Ben get the plan,' Lou says.

Hurriedly Dorothy says, 'quickly please.'

Ben peers into the bag though baby clothes and grabs the plan.

'Here it is. Is everything ok?' he asks.

Dorothy scans through the plan and tosses it to one side. As the colour drains from Helen's face, she takes a few steps back. Dorothy checks mum and notes a blood and mucus stain on the bed sheets from Lou, a vital sign that this pregnancy is moving at pace and mum's cervix is dilated and ready for imminent birth. Knowing the protocol, Dorothy checks the position of the twins. As she does her tone changes.

'Shit, shit just wait a moment...I need to get help now – press the buzzer now!'

'What's wrong, Dorothy?' Helen asks, eyes wide.

Helen then presses the buzzer hard and keeps pressing. She looks tearful and all of the colour has drained from her face, she cannot wait any longer and disappears out of the room. Another midwife, Sally Parkes, bursts through the door and Helen follows closely behind with her head down.

Sally stares at Helen. 'What am I looking at?'

'Please check the monitor and the CTG,' Dorothy instructs.

It's coming up to 2.00am and Lou is reeling with pain. Looking at the panicked faces of the midwives doesn't do anything to soothe her anxiety. By now, the family are in the twilight zone between night and day. Lou is completely knackered, and she is fading. Her face is scrunched up with pain and the monitors are beeping and, while the twins' heartbeat can be heard, it appears slower than it was.

Sally takes control.

'Helen, you go, get Cathy for me. Get her now,' she says.

'Where is she?'

'Cathy's on shift in Room 4 – go and get her and get yourself off!'

The shift is now an hour over the finish time, Helen knowing this is a bad situation, flees the scene like a bank robber jumping in the getaway car and speeding off. She knows the situation is bad and in a blink of an eyelid Helen is gone.

'OK, let's turn the TEN's up,' Sally says.

Realising that the TEN's machine is already on max and not helping with the pain, she checks baby's progress.

Lou is fully dilated.

Cathy comes into the room. Cathy is a very experienced Co-ordinating midwife and has seen just about everything in her time on the wards. She knows this is a critical situation and goes straight onto red alert. Panic is written all over her face though – this is a fast-moving event.

'Hi, Cathy, Mum is fully dilated, and the twin is in extreme foetal bradycardia,' Dorothy says.

'Oh.' Sally's face drops. 'Where are we at on the CTG?'

Cathy checks – 50 bpm.

Sally sees gaps in the CTG. It's obvious things have not progressed well and there are immediate problems. Between the two of them, they are catching up quickly on what on earth has happened in the proceeding few hours as this was an extremely high-risk birth and should have had a full team of midwives and a registrar on tap. But the timing wasn't great, and the midwife team was massively overstretched. Five minutes pass while the midwives check the CTG, plan and advise Lou on reducing pain. The TEN's machine is fully cranked so Lou is encouraged to start sucking heavily on the Entonox, NO2 & O2. Mum is fully dilated and needs to push.

A few minutes later, Cathy says, 'Call Paninakis or Randrani. We need to get the doctor to get these babies out quickly. Go and get them – just find them, go now, Quick!'

Ben checks his phone. It's 2.16am and they've been here for nearly 45 minutes. But it feels like a lifetime has passed.

The on-call registrar is already managing three births and the new on-shift Senior House Office (SHO) is the only one available and not mid birth. The midwife comes back with the SHO, Dr Paninakis. As Paninakis enters the room, it is obvious to Ben that the atmosphere has changed. The working relationship between the midwife team and the SHO is incredibly strained.

Lou is now in extreme pain, sweating profusely and screeching at Ben.

'Ben, what's happening?' she screams.

Ben says reassuringly, 'Breathe on the gas Lou, everything is ok.'

Dr Adara Paninakis tries to get a grip of the situation while the midwife attends to Lou. The SHO looks at the CTG readings and the babies' heart rates. The Dr's demeanour changes and now a slight look of panic sets in as the heart rate for the twins is below 50 bpm and the twins are now in absolute bradycardia (below 80bpm for over 12 minutes).

There is obviously beef between the Cathy, Sally and Paninakis, Ben can feel it. Cathy buzzes for the registrar or consultant – no response.

'Has the patient had the Epidural?' Paninakis enquires. Out the corner of her eye, Paninakis spots Sally pressing the buzzer. 'Why are you buzzing? Stop, I will take care of this.'

Twins were not an everyday occurrence and for the SHO, Adara saw this was a chance to prove herself and one for the CV.

Cathy is still reading through the notes to date and checks the details within the notes.

Adara mutters something under her breath and asks the midwife to prepare the stirrups ready for the birth. As Adara turns away, Sally sneakily buzzes again – nothing.

Cathy and Sally watch Adara attempt to take control of the situation and, using stern language, reminds them of her rank. It's her job to tell the midwives what she wants them to do.

'Get the patient in the stirrups so I can assess and prepare for the natural birth,' she orders.

Lou is in the final stages of labour by now and is close to passing out.

'Get me the Ventouse cap and the equipment and set it up,' Adara instructs.

'Ventouse cap? What size?' Sally asks?

'Large.'

The midwife turns to the cupboards and rustles through the equipment to get the Ventouse cup. What she pulls out looks like a toilet plunger.

'I have got this one but, looks like a small,' she says, turning it upside down to check the size.

'Small's no good. Go to the next room and get me a large like I asked, Adara barks.

Sally disappears off and moments later comes back with another packet.

'This one's a large,' she says.

'Right, prepare the equipment,' the doctor orders.

Adara then tries to attach the Ventouse to extract the baby

and, to offer a little further pain relief, infiltrates the perineum with lignocaine. Ben tries to talk to Lou who is now scared, tears falling down her sweaty red face, the pain relief just isn't enough.

Adara looks panicky, clumsy, rushed. The midwives all look apprehensive, mortified at what they're witnessing and are both glancing between the monitor and Lou. Adara cannot get the Ventouse applied and asks for Sally to get a medium cup from the other room. Out of nowhere – Cathy who had been chewing her cheek and reassuring Ben and Lou – looks sternly at Paninakis and speaks.

'We've been here before, haven't we? No more. These twins need to be delivered now.'

'Sally, you need to go now, get Dr Randrani or Dr Umbiku now, get them in here this is now a critical situation,' she continues.

Adara is still fiddling away and looks up.

'No, I can do this,' she says. 'Just go and get me a medium now please.'

Sally rushes out of the door and down the corridor and starts opening doors looking for the registrar or consultant. After checking three different rooms, she finds Randrani just closing out the delivery of a baby and almost drags him out by his arm.

'Dr we need you now, what's wrong?' he splutters.

'You need to come now – twins in three,' is all she says.

'What, why – what's the problem?'

'They are absolute bradycardic.'

'OK, can I leave you with the paperwork here – Sima come with me please.

As the three of them rush down the corridor and bang open the door, Adara is still fiddling with her head down between mum's legs, trying awkwardly to get the Ventouse cap to fit on the first twin.

Randrani has walked into total carnage. Blind incompetence, desperately ill twins, exhausted scared parents with all midwives' eyes on him. His number two, Adara, looks up at him, wishing for all of this to go away. Randrani assesses the situation like a general looking over a battlefield development plan. The SHO had been pleading with Lou to push whilst examining the head of the first twin. The registrar sets the room into a panic as he discusses the epidural and desperately needed Caesarean.

'Has Lou had her epidural?'

'No,' replies the SHO.

'Why on earth has the epidural not happened?' he demands.

Adara says, 'Can we do it now?'

Randrani angrily turns to her. 'Are you serious?! No of course not, it's too late, these babies need delivering now.'

The registrar then asks the team to set up for an immediate forceps delivery and manhandles Paninakis out of the way, removes the Ventouse and equipment. Paninakis reluctantly edges herself backwards. Dr Randrani is obviously furious but adds a feeling of calm, collected and in control to save these twins. The twins are moments from death and there's a real danger for mum that she might not make it. This is life and death. The midwives all stand ready for instructions, hanging on his every word. They fall into line just waiting for the next instruction.

'Give me the forceps,' Dr Randrani commands.

The Neville Barnes forceps are applied immediately and Randrani carries out a mediolateral episiotomy (a small surgical incision of the vaginal orifice to assist delivery). With one pull, Holly is delivered.

Holly is blue and lifeless and looks like a rag doll. Lou is now beside herself and delirious on gas and air. Almost passing out, Ben is just staring at the wall, hands on his head as Holly is whisked off to what looks like a weighing machine. Dr Randrani then concentrates on the second baby. As he prepares for the second birth the first baby's placenta is delivered which is incredibly dangerous. Randrani then engages the second twin, Ted. The heart rate is still dangerously low, the registrar's face is now ashen white. The SHO has now disappeared, so it's now the Doctor and the mixture of midwives. A second machine arrives as Holly leaves the room in an incubator-looking contraption.

There are no screams of joy, no babies crying, just total panic, and from Ben and Lou – lots of questions. Lou is asked by Dr Randrani to breathe and then push. By now, Lou is running on empty.

The second twin's head is engaged. Randrani takes no chances and applies the forceps to the second baby and, even though there is mild shoulder dystocia, performs a McRoberts manoeuvre. With one very strong pull, he yanks out Ted. The forceps have left Ted bloodied, swollen, and extremely bruised. The room is eerily silent for a place where two babies have just been born into this world.

Following the same process, Ted is put straight on the machine and oxygen masks appear. Ted is then whisked away and then nothing. Just silence.

Lou is absolutely wiped out, sweating, pale, losing a lot of blood and exhausted. Ben is traumatised and cannot speak. The doctor asks Ben if they have any clothes for the twins – Ben hands over a carrier bag full of clothes.

The staff are all silently going about their business. There is blood everywhere, like a war zone field hospital field. What should have been the perfect day has turned into a nightmare. Lou is then asked to push to deliver the second placenta. The registrar explains that the children are now in Intensive Care Unit (ICU) being well looked after and starts to stitch Lou up. The room feels empty, compassionless, and cold like a mortuary. For the staff, this is an everyday event gone wrong but for the family it was a game changer.

Ben looks up to see midwives with tears in their eyes, Lou turns to the wall and cannot speak. Adara skulks back into the room with her hands on hips like a frustrated teenager, Randrani turns to her with a face of fury and just points to the door.

'We will speak later.'

Randrani asks for the room to be cleared. He stands at the end of the bed reading the notes. Ben and Lou are now just staring at each other, absolutely devastated and shell shocked by what has just happened. Lou slips in and out of consciousness and her head then falls to one side.

'Lou, Lou? Doctor help!' Ben says.

'Lou, Lou,' Randrani repeats, checking her pupils and heart rate.

Ben stands back with his hands on his head.

'Doctor, please save her I can't lose her – please.'

The doctor then presses the buzzer. A midwife comes rushing in

'Oxygen quick and get me a shot of fludrocortisone acetate please. Blood pressure is desperately low we need to get her back and awake,' he instructs.

'Lou, Lou, wake up – can you hear me?'

Lou's out for two minutes and is really struggling. The doctor and midwife do all they can top get her back but it's a scary time and Ben is inconsolable. Lou's blood pressure starts to increase and her eyes flicker back to life, but she's incredibly pale and still breathing lightly on behind the oxygen mask.

A porter arrives and Lou is helped by the midwives into a wheelchair and is then taken through to a maternity ward. Lou has aged 20 years and looks broken by the devastation of the nights events. As the porter wheels Lou though the maternity ward, the realisation of where they are going to put Lou dawns on them both.

As Lou and Ben enter through the double doors, they realise that this is mixed maternity ward with happy parents and babies and expectant mothers.

Lou is overwhelmed and passes out in the chair. A nurse on the ward rushed to attend her. As Lou comes round, she requests the toilet and is helped by the midwives to the loo.

Ben pleads with the nursing staff that Lou be moved to a side ward or a private room but there are no rooms. They are too busy. There is nowhere for Ben, so he has to go to visitor's room to try and get a little rest. Lou and Ben are both now alone with random thoughts racing through their heads. Ben sits there, trying to get a little sleep the lights are on and with constant comings and goings and hospital 'white noise' it's almost impossible to sleep. Just as Ben drifts off, the doors burst open.

'Ben, can you come with us please?'

Ben is taken to Lou who is just staring at the wall, eyes red, pale and just glazed over.

'Have you seen the twins yet?' she asks.

Ben shakes his head. Trying to be strong, he gives her a kiss on the forehead – Lou turns away. Then a gaggle of staff arrive and close the curtain. A new lead doctor arrives; Doctor Numla Kgoale.

'We just wanted to speak to you both,' the doctor says. 'The twins are very poorly it was a difficult birth. You have both been through an awful lot this evening.'

No shit! Ben thinks. But he stays silent, just staring at the group with indignation.

'The twins are being temporarily cared for in our ICU, but ICU is full, and we are going to have to move the twins.'

Lou, tears now rolling down her cheeks, says 'No, where? Why?'

Dr Kgoale states firmly with the surrounding cast hanging on his every word 'We are full, and both babies need a lot of care.'

'Don't move my babies, I need to be with them,' Lou says.

'Really sorry but we have to move them...'

Standing their upright Ben says firmly 'When do you need to move them?'

'Tonight...'

Ben enquires 'Where to?'

'We are looking at options. Currently we have two options – Kent or Liverpool.'

'They are both hundreds of miles away,' Lou objects.

Trying to reassure the parents Dr Kgoale states 'We know but these are the only hospitals with two beds together, and the twins need specialist care. With them being twins we wanted to move them together. We may be able to get a closer hospital, but they would have to go separately.'

'No, they cannot go separately! They have to be together,' Lou says, distraught.

'They need to I am afraid as they are not in permanent beds at the moment, and we have other babies coming back from planned surgery in the morning and we need the space. Do you have a preference?'

Ben slumps into the chair with his head in his hands

'My Uncle lives in Manchester, but we have no relatives in Kent or Liverpool,' he says.

'We have to move quickly as time is of the essence...' the registrar says.

Lou and Ben cannot decide and say they need to be with the twins.

The registrar explains it's best to be near a relative so Liverpool would be the best option as it's close to Manchester.

'They have 2 beds available'. Do you agree please?'

Lou and Ben think for a moment.

'We need to get this moving and the team can then make the arrangements for the twins to be moved separately.'

'We have no choice, do we?' Lou says.

'It will have to be Liverpool.' Ben agrees.

'When will they go?' Ben asks the doctor.

The doctor fires back 'In the next few hours.'

Lou enquires 'Can we go with them?'

'Unfortunately, not, as we need a team in each ambulance, we will move the twins and arrange for you to go in the morning, you both need to rest.' The Doctor confirms.

'Can we not go with them?' Lou asks again.

The Doctor tentatively replies 'Ideally, we need to look after you. You really need to sleep, and we will arrange for you go to separately as you have lost a lot of blood.'

'Ben?' Lou looks at her husband.

'We need to see the twins now and we are going with them,' Ben says.

'They are heavily sedated due to the medication,' the doctor warns.

Lou then firmly states to the Doctor 'We need to see them, and we need to be with them.'

The Doctor staring at the wall lets the parents know 'There's a lot going on around the twins at the moment.'

'No, I am sorry I need to see them both before they go. I must!' Lou says, defiant.

'OK, but it will need to be brief whilst we prepare for the journey.'

Lou is wheeled to ICU by a porter with Ben following closely behind. The porter is talking but it's a one-way conversation.

This is the first time Ben & Lou have seen the twins. Both are tubed and wired in incubators, fully reliant on all the tubes and wires to stay alive.

'Ben I cannot believe this is happening,' Lou whispers.

'I know, I know.'

Ben stares at the beautiful babies behind Perspex glass. There are pipes, tubes, and cables everywhere. The pale bodies look so fragile in just oversized nappies and hand-made woollen hats. This is seismic and today has changed everything forever. With his hand over his mouth, Ben screeches in pain.

After the brief visit, the couple are then escorted to a waiting room while they wait for the ambulances. Ben and Lou sit in the same room but in their half-asleep, half-awake state, not a word is said.

'Right, we are ready to go, ' the doctor informs them.

As the first twin is wheeled to the first ambulance the team explain there has been a delay with the second ambulance, and they have to go separately.

'No way,' Lou screams at them. 'They are not leaving without their mother! Ben, I have to go in the first Ambulance, we are not leaving before the other ambulance is here'.

There is a tense stand-off as they wait for the second ambulance.

Two seriously ill babies, two exhausted and terrified parents, and six medial staff just doing their job. All in silence, waiting to transport the precious and fragile babies for their first unwelcome journey with paramedics and nurses in tow.

Every minute seems to pass like hours. Then the second ambulance reverses into the bay. Ben travels with Holly and Lou travels with Ted. Two members of specialist staff travel with Ben, Lou, and the twins.

Thirty minutes have passed as they sit there, knackered in silence. Together but a million miles apart deep in thought and dread. They are wheeled to the ambulances and start the hundred- and ten-mile trip to Liverpool.

Chapter 2
Time Standing Still

As they leave Nottingham hospital in the hours between night and day, Lou falls asleep sat uncomfortably in her wheelchair with her hand glued to the Perspex case surrounding the incubator. Other than the sound of the road noise echoing around the ambulance over the bip's, and bleeps, Ted is oblivious to the world around him, heavily sedated with his swollen eyes tightly shut, intubation tube pressing up against his button nose into his mouth in between his pale pink lips.

In the other ambulance, Ben is fast sleep sat closely to Holly with a green blanket wrapped tightly around him. The nursing staff sit vigilantly watching every dial and screen, monitoring the first 24 hours of these precious children's life.

Dawn is breaking and the sun appears through the clouds. It is now well and truly a new dawn for Ben, Lou, and family as they speed to Liverpool. The beginning of a new day that Ben and Lou could never in their wildest dreams ever of contemplated. They still haven't fully processed the implications.

The ambulances hit commuter traffic coming into

Liverpool and turn on the blues and twos. Lou wakes with a jolt, her hand still loosely touching the Perspex. The journey to Liverpool seems to have taken for ever. The ambulance sirens are blaring and the speed increases and decreases as the traffic intensifies.

Exhausted, Ben has drifted off and is fast on. As weaves through the traffic avoiding the cars splitting like the red sea the ambulances swerves violently to the left and as it does. Ben wakes to sound of the beeps and blips of the machine's keeping Holly alive. Ben shakes his head and runs his fingers through is mop of hair and rubs his red eyes. Both children have remained motionless throughout their journey, heavily sedated though intravenous lines both being fed through a nasogastric tube. Ben wakes and hopes it's just been a bad nightmare, but he looks over to see Holly wired up inside the incubator, so pure and vulnerable relying on mechanical intervention to even breath. The nurse with her has been up all night.

'Good morning,' she says.

'Morning. How is Holly?'

'Stable.'

'OK. How long before we get there?

'Not far now.'

As Ben starts to think about home, he glances as his phone – 10% battery and no charger. Ben starts to get anxious about making all of the necessary arrangements and being so far from home. Thoughts turn to their home routine, to Megan, Jake, Terri and calling his parents but he just knew he would fall apart on the phone, so he texts both sets of parents as they drive through the unfamiliar streets of Liverpool with the sun piercing through the buildings.

Neighbour Terri gets a text about day-to-day routines and that they won't be back, and his mum and dad will be in touch.

To the grandparents, he texts:

Things haven't gone very well......the children are not in

good shape we are on our way to Liverpool.
Will call when I know more.

His phone pings and he glances down.

Oh darling, Liverpool?
Yes, there are no beds so we are on our way, will call later.
Can you call Terri and pick the kids up please.
OK, we're thinking and praying for you all. I am sure the twins will be fine and it's just a precaution?
Call us later!

Ben looks down at his phone – missed calls and messages from work. He texts his boss, letting him know he won't make London and needs time with his family.

He ignores all of the other texts except Henrietta, Lou's sister. Hetty had sent a text.

Great night last night thanks to both, hope Lou is well and looking forward to meeting the beautiful twins, not long now....XXXXXX

Hi, Hetty, we are on our way to Liverpool, twins not well. Will text later. XX

Oh darling, sorry to hear this. Please keep me in touch XXXX

Will do XX

As they arrive at the hospital gates together, the ambulances are met at the door by a large group of staff all in different coloured uniforms confidently rushing around and asking all sorts of questions. Ben notices the warm Liverpudlian accents as they are welcomed in. At speed, the staff wheel the children up to the ICU. A kind nurse caringly introduces herself as

Róisín. The parents are taken to a private room where Lou is helped from her chair to a bed. They are left alone together for the first time in hours. Four walls, lots of tears, utterances of 'why us' and wondering questions – could they have done more, what went wrong? Was it their fault? What happened in that last nightmare hour?

Ben sits in the blue sterile hospital chair and stares out the window..., Lou is in bed, just staring at the wall.

The room is a silent, soulless atmosphere with both parents in absolute disbelief. As time passes, unknown to both Ben and Lou, they fall asleep – unable to keep their eyes open any longer.

Róisín comes back into the room sometime later, opening the door really carefully in case the parents were asleep, but Lou is on patrol and wakes in an instant.

'Hi Róisín.' Ben rubs his bleary eyes.

'How are you both?'

Ben chirps up, 'How do you think?!'

'Ben that's not helping. Sorry Róisín, we are both extremely tired and traumatised about what's happened,' Lou says.

'I know it's a worrying time for you both, the twins are in the best of care here.' Róisín assures her. 'Can I take a look down below?'

'Sure, I think the medication is wearing off. It's very sore.'

'OK, yes, I can see that you have had an episiotomy so the stitches will pull a bit,' Róisín confirms. 'I will give you some more medication and then we can go and see the twins once they are settled in.'

'I need the loo, Róisín.'

'Ben, help me get Lou up and to the toilet please,' Róisín instructs.

Lou winces in pain as she pees for the first time since the delivery.

Róisín reassures Lou to keep going and it will get better, Lou grips her arm tightly as she comes to the end of her peeing.

'You're doing great Lou,' Róisín says. 'Ben, can you come

and help please.'

Ben and Róisín put Lou back into the wheelchair and Róisín leaves the room.

Knackered, Ben looks out of the window still going over what's happened. He stares at his phone – 8% battery. Lou return to just staring at the wall – she cannot remove the blank expression on her face.

Róisín and a nurse come back into the room.

'Hi, are you both up to seeing the twins now they are in ICU?' Róisín asks.

'Yes please, can we take the birth toys for them?' Lou asks.

'Yes of course. Let's you get back into your chair and get going!'

Ben and Lou had bought the twins soft toys, Beany Dog and Ducky as Ben had named them before he put them in the overnight birthing bag. They brought them to comfort the twins and wanted to give them something from the day to remember. It wasn't meant to be like this, Ducky and Beany Dog feel like a pathetic offering under the circumstances.

Ben and Lou are led off and down to ICU. As they walk, pushing Lou's wheelchair in total silence through the long sterile corridors, Ben, and Lou have tunnel vision – everything around them is just a blur. They arrive on ICU. As Róisín pings her pass on the door security sensor the other nurse pushes open the door. As Ben and Lou survey the room of 14 babies the atmosphere is intense. The cold sterile atmosphere is broken only by the now familiar blips and beeps like a Skegness amusement arcade. It's totally overwhelming, there are 3-4 nurses per baby – cables and towers of machines loom over the tiny Perspex bubbles preserving human life. Finally, they get to see the twins. As they approach the babies at the end of the long, crowded room, tears stream down Lou's cheeks. Her eyes though are firmly fixed on the twins with a determined 'I am here to fight with you' mothers' stoicism. Ben shuffles behind, looking round the room in absolute astonishment that this world exists. What has happened to their perfect world in sunny West Bridgford? This is an earth-shattering event, a life changing moment in their existence – – things will never be the same again.

As they get closer to the twins with apprehension, they look into the Perspex incubators. The twins' faces are still covered in pipes, intubation tubes strapped their mouths, labels on wrists and tubes coming out of their noses. Oversized nappies half cover the tiny babies with just their little legs and bare chests kept warm by the ambient Perspex box. The babies are still lifeless with their eyes bruised, swollen, and closed. Their fists are clenched like they are telling Ben and Lou how helpless, angry, and how determined they are. The twins are wearing their hats and booties the parents had bought for them. Clothing accessories that were there to wrap the children in warmth on the entry into the world. A day that was no-one ever conceived could happen, if only they could they turn back time...

They ask if the toys can be put into the incubator and the nurses say they can, but they need to be sanitised first. The nurses explain that they can open the little side door and place the toys behind the twins as to not move the life supporting array of tubes and cables.

They both have their moment.

Lou nestles Beany Dog up against Holly's motionless body and cannot resist just briefly touching her back, warm to the touch and as soft as silk. Lou's head tilts and a very small smile beams across Lou's tearful face. Ben opens Ted's incubator and touches his arm, leaving his hand there for a fleeting moment. His eyes glazed and watering, he places Ducky at the back of Ted and touches Ted's woollen hat and then pulls out as the nurse shuts the door. Both parents look at each other and a very small smile pierces through there tired and tearful faces. Ben moves towards Lou and from behind and hugs her, crying and squeezing. Lou resiliently kisses Ben on the side of the head, but her eyes are firmly fixed on the twins. Róisín lets the parents know that the doctor will be doing his rounds shortly if they want to wait and ask any questions.

The parents glance from one incubator to the other – completely spaced out, waiting in limbo for some positive news.

'Can I hold them? Lou asks.

'Not at the moment I am afraid,' explains the nurse. 'The Doctor will be on her rounds shortly and will explain the next steps.'

Lou's head sinks down, tired, and exhausted gathering all her strength to take the news, whatever it may be, from the doctors.

Moments pass and then over the din of the machines, at end of the room through the double doors the Paediatrician and her entourage appear with a gaggle of wannabe doctors hanging on the Paediatrician's every word.

The ward is high intensity, blips and bips going off all around. Nurses checking notes, hourly feeds and administering medication keeping each precious life alive. Each bed gets around 10 minutes either talking to nurses, parents, or both with life-changing information and the unknown. All of the parents on ICU look zombified. Some are new to the ward; some have been here for days or even weeks, so each is in a different mind-set and level of exhaustion and hope. Critical, life-changing information is being delivered by a human just doing their job, a conveyor belt of 10-minute conversations with lifetime implications for the receiver.

As the throng makes its way to the first incubator and the first twin, Holly, the Paediatrician Introduces herself as Dr Sangrita. Her tone is confident and reassuring. Ben and Lou are hanging on her every word. Dr Sangrita speaks slowly and with surety to allow the parents to understand clearly and honestly where they are.

'Hi, my name is Dr Sangrita. I am the senior paediatrician here at Alder Hey. This is Holly, yes?'

The parents nod.

'I have checked the delivery notes from last night, you have all been through quite an ordeal.'

'Yes, we have, what can you tell us Doctor?' Lou asks.

'Holly is very poorly and has suffered from acute Hypoxia, suffering a significant brain injury which may lead to a condition called Cerebral Palsy but it's very early to tell.'

Lou gasps, all the colour draining from her face. Those two words; brain and injury, together are as bad as it gets. Cancer you can fight but the brain cannot be 100% fixed. Lou is computing this in the seconds she has to respond. Ben is similarly absorbing what has just been explained about his children, trying to understand what Cerebral Palsy actually means but the words will not come out. His mouth is open his eyes just piercing though Dr Sangrita's like she is lying to him. Only hours old and the twins are already fighting for their little lives. Ben and Lou both feel like they are in someone else's nightmare and that this is not reality – definitely not their reality.

'Will Holly's condition improve?' Lou stammers.

'We are unsure at this stage. I have to be honest with both of you.'

The assembled gaggle of doctors in training and nurses all have blank faces and are clinging onto every word and making notes about how this news is being delivered. One day it might be them. They all know that the prognosis is bad. Brain injury outcomes are rarely good and Cerebral Palsy can display itself mentally and physically in many different ways but it a potential life changing condition. For some, they have not seen this devastating news delivered before and only read about it in textbooks in training.

'Why did this happen?' Ben demands.

'Again, from the notes, I am unsure and have been in touch with Nottingham to get more details. They have passed all the information onto Dr Vaughan who I am speaking to later. My main concern here is focused on the twins to ensure we stabilize them both to allow us to move forward. We need to get them off the epileptic seizure drugs to see how they react.

This will be done gradually and slowly with strict monitoring.'

'OK,' Ben whispers.

The doctor then talks to the nurses caring for the twins, asking questions relating to the medication and how the night had gone.

Lou and Ben are hanging on to every word to try and demystify the conversation and terminology , which is almost impossible as the condition of the twins is so complex. The Paediatrician then moves over to Ted and starts to look at the notes and talk to the attending nurses.

'How is Ted doing, Dr?' Lou asks.

'Ted is stable but again we need to see how the next few hours play out.'

'Will the twins improve enough to allow me to breast feed?'

'Difficult to say at this point. We are medicating to control the seizures with phenobarbitone and Phenytoin. We just need to take it hour by hour,' the doctor says. 'Have you expressed yet?'

'Expressed?' Lou says, confused.

'Expressed any breast milk?'

'No.'

'Do you want to give the twins breast milk or formula?'

'Breast-milk, ideally'

'Can you express some milk, and we can give this to the twins?'

'I don't know how to do that.'

'Róisín?' the doctor summons.

Róisín reassures Lou that she will show her how to do it with a breast pump.

Ben then steps forward and asks Dr Sangrita, 'Will they improve Doctor? What are the chances of a full recovery from this, when will they wake up?'

'We just cannot say at this point. We need to take each hour and each day as it comes with both Ted and Holly.' Dr Sangrita says. 'Both have had an extremely tough time during birth, and we just need time. Both the twins are in the best of care, and you will be looked after whilst you are with us.'

'When can we hold them?' Lou asks again.

'We will arrange a private moment to get this arranged at some point today.'

Tears fall down Lou's cheeks as she tries to be strong for the twins, but she cannot stop the tears and wearily pleas with the doctor. 'I need to hold my babies.'

'I totally understand.' Dr Sangrita turns to the nurses. 'Please make this happen today.'

The white coated gaggle then move onto the next bed. Dr Sangrita has delivered her news and, as bad as it is, Ben and Lou needed to hear it. The fact they can hold their babies offers a little hope. This gave them added resolve, they will be there for both Holly and Ted and give them both all they need for the very best outcome.

Róisín then clasps Lou's wheelchair handles and gently requests that they all go back to the ward to rest, and they can express milk for the twins.

As they make their way back through the unit, Ben and Lou seem miles apart, splintered, distant & deeply wounded, like strangers living a nightmare.

Chapter 3

The Call No One Ever Wants to Make

As they arrive back in the room, Ben and Lou talk for the first time. In a moment of clarity, Lou then goes into mum mode; 'Can you ring your mum to go and fetch the kids from next door? We need to get them to school.' she says. 'Lunch, concert tickets, uniform... Jake tie!'

Ben reassures her, 'Lou, it will be fine. Between Terri and my parents, Jake and Megan will be fine don't worry. I have sorted it this morning.'

'Ben, I need you to call your parents, we need to make plans, we're miles from home and the children won't know what's going on...'

'I will call them all and sort it. Have you got your charger with you I only have 4% left?'

'No. Why have you not got yours?' Lou snaps.

'I will ask Róisín.'

Ben goes outside for the first time. He breathes in the fresh spring air.

Ben looks down at his phone – 12 missed calls and 6 voicemails and 4% battery. This is the call he's been dreading.

Ben struggles to actually look into his favourites to find Hannah, mum and press 'MUM', knowing the emotion that is about to wash over him. As he dials, he looks out at the ambulances coming and going, scores of ambulances parked, staff in an array of uniforms coming to and from work and patients and carers filing in and out of the doors.

As the phone rings, his heart is racing, and his mouth is dry.

'Hi darling.'

'Hi mum!' His voice crackles and breaks. He tries desperately to hold it together but, cannot. Ben holds the phone away temporarily with his hand over his mouth trying desperately to hold it in. 'Mum?'

'Yes darling?'

Ben's mum's reassuring tone is too much for Ben. He is sobbing and cannot breathe. He takes a few moments to compose himself, focusing on the trees swaying in the wind.

'Darling, are you there?'

'Mum, the twins are really unwell.'

'What's happened, Ben?'

'The children had a really bad time at the hospital in Nottingham,' he explains. 'They were staved of oxygen and may have brain damage.'

'Brain damage – oh no Ben.'

Now Ben is struggling to even talk and cannot hold it together. He just walks round in circles with his hand clasped across his mouth – unable to speak. He knew how much this would hurt his mum and all their family and friends.

'Take your time Ben,' she says, but her voice is breaking.

Hannah starts to cry, unable to console her son, understand the seriousness of the situation or as a loving mum fix it.

'Please, how can we help? How's Lou?' Hannah asks.

'Mum, Lou is in pain and being incredibly strong. The twins are in intensive care with wires and cables everywhere, I cannot help then, I feel totally helpless. Can you help with Jake and Megan.'

'I checked this morning at home on Jake and Megan, but no one was in?' Hannah says.

'Terri next door will have them. Can you go round and let Terri know later you will them up from school. I don't know when we're coming back.'

'Yes darling, of course. I have Terri's number I will call and sort the children. I have a spare set of keys.'

'Thanks, Mum. Please, we need your help.'

'Look after yourself. We will work through this. I am sure it's just a temporary measure and the hospital are just being cautious; they will be working out what to do next.' she says. 'What do you want me to tell Jake and Megan?'

'Please don't tell them how serious it is, just let them know they are just unwell.'

'Will do, Ben.'

'Thanks mum, will text later.'

'OK darling. Please look after each other, bye...'

Ben presses the red button to end the call, still wiping away the tears. The fear is now starting to take stock. Sitting on the step, Ben contemplates what is to come and what might have been. Extreme physical exhaustion from lack of sleep and emotional exhaustion – Ben's brain is mushed.

He looks down at his phone and checks his voicemails. As he scrolls, he sees one from Hetty. He opens the message and puts on loudspeaker. Ben cannot even speak.

"Ben," she opens.

"Hi Hetty," he replies.

"Hi darling I wanted to send my love to you both and the twins. All will be well darling; we are here for you and will do whatever is needed."

Ben sobs uncontrollably – Hetty's familiar tone is sturdy and loving. This is just what Ben needed. "Hets, the twins are really ill we don't know whether they are going to make it."

"Ben, we all need to be strong and positive."

Still sobbing Ben replies; "I know Hets, but they are very, very poorly."

"What have the doctors said?"

"That they may be brain damaged."

"Brain damage varies. We have to be positive."

"I know Hets, but I am struggling."

"Ben, I am here for you darling—

Ben's phone finally dies, and they are cut off.

Ben walks in circles for a while around the memorial garden to appear strong for Lou. When he makes his way back to the room, Lou is staring out of the window from her bed, numb with the pain of the events. The pain relief is wearing off. As Ben walks back into the hospital passing the smokers sat, stood, and perched at the hospital entrance he thinks to himself how ironic it is that chronically ill patients on drips are smoking themselves to death at the hospital. Ben quizzes himself on naming the band that had a song called 'Smokers outside the hospital doors'. This keeps him occupied as he walks back to the ward. Ben walks back to the room and Lou is resting. Lou gently opens her eyes.

"How are the kids doing?" she asks.

"All is fine. Mum and Terri have them all sorted. Please don't worry."

"Who's picking them up?"

"Mum," Ben replies.

"Does she know it's cricket practice tomorrow?"

"No, I will text her. I just need to charge my phone."

"I need to express milk for the twins. I want to give them the very best start. Can you call Róisín back so I can see how to use the equipment?" Lou asks.

"Yes, I will go and find her".

Ben comes back and explains she's coming and grabs Lous limp hand.

As Róisín walks back in the room with the equipment Ben asks, "Do you have a charger, Róisín?"

"Yes, I will get it, one moment,"

The midwife shows Lou how to attach the pump and Lou starts to express the milk.

"How much do we need?" Lou asks.

"Express what you can, and we can put it in the fridge and give the twins through their feeding tube in ICU."

Ben stands there powerless. Róisín hands Ben the expressed milk and asks that he decants to the bottles on the side. Lou has been leaking and expresses 3 bottles. "Ben, label them and go and put in the fridge in the kitchen please straight away. Grab a coffee or tea whilst you are there?" Róisín says.

"Do you want a brew, Lou?" Ben asks.

"No, not for me."

"Róisín?"

"No, thank you."

Ben does as his told and goes to the kitchen.

Ben opens the fridge and, moving the labelled sandwich boxes, nestles the bottles in the fridge. He sticks the kettle on and makes a brew. As Ben stands there waiting for the kettle to boil, he thinks about the party at the house. He then steps through the events, his stomach-churning thinking about the future and the fact that he expected to be back at work today and moving on. Bringing the twins home, the joy, cards, christening, friends, and relatives popping in for coffee and cake. A proud dad showing off his perfect family. The holidays and academic achievements the kids would all make and finally having the snip as this was job done. The click of the kettle brings his fantasying to an end along with his misplaced thoughts of the future.

He walks back to the room with his brew. Expressing is now complete and Róisín adjusts Lou's cushions.

Ben stands there with his brew, trying to be supportive, talking about normal home stuff and reassuring Lou that Jake and Megan are being looked after and heaping praise on Lou for being so strong, his voice faltering as the emotions take the better of him.

Lou isn't really listening or replying. Róisín is making sure everything they need is in the room and gets extra bottles, labels, and Lanolin for Lou's sore nipples. Róisín then goes to clean the equipment. As she leaves, she praises Lou and lets her know she is doing great and that she will take the milk to the twins and asks Ben to just contact her if she needs any help.

Ben has his moment.

Taking a deep breath, he says, "Lou you are amazing, we will get through this."

"Please Ben. Can we not talk about what's just happened? Please, not now. I need to ensure the twins get what they need. I need to be close to the twins they need us right now."

Ben deflates. "Just rest Lou and I will call Róisín later."

He slides the chair closer to Lou puts his hand out to her. As their hands meet, Lou pulls hers away. She turns away and quickly drifts off to sleep. Ben sighs and then drifts off himself.

Ben is first to wake and looks lovingly at Lou who is still peacefully asleep. He lets Lou sleep and quietly moves around the room. As Lou's eyes open, he gives her a kiss on the lips. By now its mid-afternoon and the room is warm and clammy.

"Ben, can you call Róisín?" Lou says as she wakes.

Róisín walks back into the room.

"Can we go and see the twins now please? I need to hold them." Lou says as Róisín walks back into the room.

"Leave it with me. I will call the unit."

Róisín disappears and then comes back.

"Good news. They are ready for you. But I want you try for the loo first and then we will go."

The three make their way up to ICU. As the doors open, they again enter now familiar sights and sounds of ICU. Its respectfully and eerily quiet. The twins are at the end of the room and, as Róisín wheels Lou closer, Lou feels that intricate maternal bond with her children. Ben slowly walks behind them in his head praying for the good news he wants; *everything's ok and they're awake, and we were wrong*. As the wheelchair comes to a standstill, Róisín clicks the brakes on.

Róisín talks to the nurses to get an update.

"Still stable," comes the report.

"Did you give them the milk?" Róisín asks.

"Yes, they are taking the milk through the tube."

"Right. Are we able to get the twins out?"

"Yes, but let's do it slowly. We need to position mum and dad carefully close to the incubators and feed the wires together."

Holly is the first to be manoeuvred out from behind the Perspex. As the Perspex cover is moved the nurses gently bring Holly up. Two nurses lift and guide the baby, cables, monitors, and intubation tubes towards Lou sat beaming at this first hold. There are no more tears left. Holly is gently lowered into position and into the Lou's outstretched arms. It's a beautiful sight, but Ben feels like a spare part, not knowing where to put himself.

As Lou holds Holly around the tubes Lou prises open Holly's fist, clenched due to the seizures, she places her finger in Holly's tiny hand and Holly momentarily squeezes Lou's finger. It's the first moment, the first connection. Lou moves to kiss Holly and breathe in the new-born baby smell.

Lou looks up for Ben and almost in unison they both share a smile and a single tear of parental joy, both heads are just bowed down gazing down at Holly.

Time stands still for Lou as she looks into Holly's bruised face, eyes tightly closed. The smell of a new baby is like nothing else, and Lou just cannot stop breathing it in. Holly's face is blank, expressionless, her body is floppy and so small it can be cupped in one hand. The nappy is almost bigger than the baby. The nurses turn to Ben and ask if he wants to hold Holly. Ben says he is fine and just strokes Holly's head with a huge grin across his face. He could only think of Megan at this moment; when he first held her and the beautiful girl, she has grown into.

"We need to put her back in now, is that OK?" one of the nurses asks.

Lou looks up, delivers one last kiss and nods with a proud smile. This bonding experience is everything for Lou. As they gently lift Holly back into the safety of her Perspex box, Lou is wheeled over to Ted's Incubator. Ted is then prepared and lifted into Lou's waiting arms. Ted is sedated like Holly so there is just an expressionless look on his face. Lou kisses Ted's forehead and speaks into his ear. The nurses are cancelling out the bip's and bleeps to try and give Lou and Ben a moment of peace with their new-borns but, it's impossible to keep this intense room quiet for even a moment. Lou wants this moment to last forever and, cupping Ted, holds him into her neck. Lou listens for a breath or a noise but there's nothing. It's all mechanically controlled with Ted's tiny chest moving up and down.

"Can we get Ted back into his Incubator?" one of the nurses says.

Lou reluctantly hands Ted back to the waiting nurses with one last word for Ted; 'love you, baby'. Lou now feels in control – the mother's bond is made. Ben feels strongly distant, just as he did with the Jake and Megan. Ben only felt attachment to both from 4 years old and his bond was through sport. He is struggling with the attachment parenting Lou practised and only really bonded with Jake and Megan later in life when they could do something that he enjoyed. Ben really struggled when the kids were under 4, the tantrums, lack of ability and mess. He felt very un-paternal until they reached 4 and then started to bond as long as it didn't affect his social and work life.

As the parents sit looking at the babies in the safety of their Perspex bubbles, they are both thinking the same thing: Life will never be the same again.

This successful, high achieving, well liked, happy couple are now in a new world. Their old life in suburban bliss being judged by their and their kids' achievements, success, and financial standing are now a distant memory. Their perceived perfect life has crashed to the ground in 30 minutes. Controlling their life with money, status or confidence will not save them now – they are in unknown territory, and they are scared and powerless.

Thoughts are racing through their minds but very different mindsets.

Lou's thoughts are nurturing:

How can I be the best mother possible at this point in the twins' life and what do I need to do to make this situation better?
I can make this better.
I need to be close to my babies.
I can do this.
I need to be resilient.
Make sure I ask the right questions.
I need my family all together and I need to be at home.

Ben's thoughts are more selfish and irrational.
Will they live?
How bad are the twins going to be?
How will our friends react?
What does this mean for me and Lou?
What about family how will they react?
How will work react I still want a career?
Should we let them go?
Can we give the twins up for adoption?
How will we cope!

Both are deep in their silent thoughts, like living nightmare, when you fall from a building but never hit the floor; powerless and useless.

As they gather their thoughts and feelings, Róisín comes back into the room and reassures them again, encouraging them both to rest and they will be seeing the doctors again later.

"When can they be with us in the room and out of ICU, Róisín?" Lou asks.

"Hard to say really, we are just taking it by the hour. They are sedated and in the very best care. The risk of seizures, we have had to slightly increase the medication."

"Epileptic seizures? That sounds bad. Oh god, is that normal?" Lou asks, her anxiety rising.

Visions of the twins frothing at the mouth and writhing on the floor are going through both parents' minds – this is brand new territory for both.

"With the trauma they suffered, yes, sometimes it is." Róisín says. "What will happen is as the days pass is they will reduce gradually the medication until the children are not showing signs of seizures, weaning them off."

*

What should be such a precious moment in the lives of the family feels so distant and all Lou wants is to hold them, protect them and be next to them.

As Róisín leaves the room, Ben and Lou are left on their own again.

"You ok, Lou?" Ben asks.

"I just don't want to talk at the moment. My mind is racing, and I just want to be with the twins. I need to sleep."

"I'll go and get a coffee and let you sleep."

Lou turns her head away from Ben, closes her eyes and drifts off to sleep.

As Ben leaves the room, he picks up his charged phone and wanders down to the canteen area to contact family and, more importantly, Hetty. Ben needs some love. Lou pushing Ben away is alien to him and he doesn't recognise his own wife. Ben texts through to ensure Megan and Jake are OK and then starts a text thread to Hetty. He smiles as the replies come back. They are gushy and loving to both Ben and Lou. He needs this. He needs to feel constantly loved and craves female approval. This is something he has developed over his life from his adoring mum Ben has always joked about his views on a polygamous relationship with Lou and another woman.

This has been an earth shattering 24 hours.

Chapter 4

Coming Home to Reality

The twins are gently being weaned off their medication. Slowly and steadily to see how they react and to ensure the seizures don't start again. Still tube fed, Lou is expressing milk now twice a day to keep up with the demands. Ben has been sleeping in the visitors room now for days and needs to go home. Jake and Megan have been passed around between family and Terri to ensure they continue a little normality. Róisín has been around when she is on shift and incredibly helpful and warm as all of the staff have helping the family deal with this living nightmare. Both twins are incredibly poorly but at least Lou is able to hold them once a day between the tubes, pipes and cables maintaining life.

Liverpool has a discrete mother and baby unit off the main wards with assistance and this is the goal, a new normal. Surrounded by this professional loving help, Lou does not feel ready for home yet and needs the comfort of this team. Ben and Lou take photos and a few videos of the vulnerable and helpless babies surrounded by their Perspex life support. Worried parents come and go, and the patients, parents and visitors are transient, ever changing. Day and night merge into one for Ben and Lou. They have no idea how long they have been there, the time of day or the weather. Ben now is on first name terms with most of the staff and has his 'usual breakfast, lunch and dinner'. His coffee is ready as he approaches the counter. Ben is knackered, Lou is fighting it and determined to be there 24/7 for her babies.

Ben then approaches Lou and asks about going home to get a change of clothes, restock and see the children. Ben and Lou have been solo through this, although they are physically close to Ben's Uncle Frank, he has too much on at work and wishes them all the best. Uncle Frank is an emotionless character with no fatherly or loving instinct. His work is his passion and money his master. Lou gives Ben a long list of things to do and what she needs when he returns. It needs to be a 24-hour dash. Ben leaves the security of the hospital, blinking into the daylight as he waits for his taxi – he is speechless, tired and on an emotional knife edge. As the black cab pulls away, emotion comes over him like a wave, he is uncontrollable, crying and sobbing. The cab driver in his deep Scouse accents checks on Ben who cannot speak and just nods, he cannot get the words out, his mouth disconnected from his brain. Ben cries from the hospital to the station, thoughts racing thought his head. He had tried to be so strong around Lou and the medical staff and but now an avalanche of hopelessness engulfs him. The quickest route back by train is almost 7 hours. Ben cannot believe that a two- and half-hour journey can take so long, but he sucks it up and gets the ticket. As the train pulls in, Ben feels a sense of home, back where he feels familiarity. He jumps in a cab and as he leaves the station and catches out of the corner of his eye a sign for the cities hospital. It gives Ben a strange feeling of bitterness and anger. The very place that brought so much joy to him and Lou is now tarnished.

Opening the front door, he is greeted by Lou's mum, Felicity, who hugs him and asks how they all are. Lou's dad, Henry is upstairs with Megan and Jake. Felicity says she will get the children down. Ben sinks into the sofa and then the door bursts open with both children running at him. Ben holds them and cries uncontrollably. Both children take a few steps back, Ben is making strange noises of grief that they have not heard before. Jake and Megan are confused and are not sure what's going on as they have not been told much. As Ben attempts to control himself, he brings the children in again for another hug. Megan is deeply shaken by her dad's appearance and the outpouring of emotion she has never been seen from him before. Jake is confused as he idolises his dad who has always been very dismissive and churlish with regards to men and boys showing emotion. What has happened to his hero? Ben explains to both children that mum is fine, but their new brother and sister are very poorly but will be home soon. That is about all Ben can say and then he starts to cry again. Felicity and Henry are stood in the doorway, speechless. Henry takes the children back upstairs and Felicity sits with Ben, comforting him and listening.

Felicity is a good soul and does all she can to extract details out of Ben and check on her daughter and new grandchildren. Felicity just wants to know when they will all be back, Henry reassures the children that all will be OK, even though he knows it won't be and this is the start of a massive change. Ben is aware that he is scruffy and needs to go for a shower. It feels like a lifetime has passed since he was last in his bathroom and it feels strangely familiar, like a lucid dream. He showers, changes, and gets his list that Lou had prepared and starts to pack ready for the morning. He goes in and gives the kids a kiss and makes his way down the stairs, refreshed and like he is back in the real world. Felicity has started his favourite dinner, spaghetti Bolognese with extra red wine and Maggi sauce with Marks and Spencer garlic bread. The smell of home cooking is comforting. He sits down at the counter and talks to Felicity and Henry about all they know so far. He cannot give a date for a full return but reassures it won't be long. Ben manages to not cry as he explains the night and what's happened in Liverpool.

Felicity and Henry just listen and cannot comprehend the enormity of what's happened or the long-term consequences. They naively still think the twins will pull through and this is just a temporary blip.

Ben then makes his excuses to go up and finish packing as he needs to be up at 5.30am start the drive back to Liverpool to deliver 'the list' and be there for Lou and the twins.

Ben's alarm goes off and he gets up, eyes still half shut, having an unbroken night's sleep. Looking in the mirror, a broken man stares back. Ben grabs the last few bits, piles them into the bag and slowly and quietly walks down the stairs. As he walks past the kids' room, Jake is at the door in his dressing gown holding his Buzz Lightyear toy. Ben kisses him on the forehead and tells him everything is going to be ok and ushers him back to bed. As he watches Jake climb into bed, he blows him a kiss with a tear in his eye. Ben and Jake both know from this moment that their relationship, inseparable you couldn't get a cigarette paper between them, has changed forever. Ben closes the door behind him and heads into the dawn air, birds still singing at the top of their small lungs. Ben gets in the car, holds the steering wheel, and takes a massive breath in and then out, texts Lou to say, 'on way'.

The journey is full of thought and reflection on the family that was and the future and what it will bring. A brief stop at the drive through Starbucks and onto Liverpool. As he pulls in, his heart is pounding, and he sucks up the £25 a day parking not knowing how long they will be there for. He enters the hospital entrance, past the drip-stand-holding smokers and dressing-gown-clad patients. He doesn't need a map as he knows almost every corridor back to the ICU by now. As he gets there, he finds Lou who has a million questions about Jake and Megan and goes through her list to ensure nothing is forgotten.

Lou then lets Ben know that Holly is off most of the anti-convulsant drugs but still on breathing tubes and sedated. They are waiting for the doctor but hoping that the sedation will start to be withdrawn that day. Ted is still very unwell and will remain on what he is for a few days. Ben shares delight at that Holly could be opening her swollen eyes for the first time. A glimmer of hope. The posse of doctors and hangers-on enter the ICU. They discuss with the doctor next steps and the doctor is keen to get Holly off sedation and remove the tube. They explain that it would be good if Lou and Ben were not present as removing the intubation tube is a brutal procedure for parents to witness but say they can be close by and see Holly when her eyes are open. Lou sheds a tear of joy that one of the twins can make the next small step. They ask about Ted and the doctor explains that they need to get Ted to the same stage where Holly is now before they can follow the same steps. As the doctors leave, Lou and Ben share an embrace and a kiss.

Lou is up and walking but still in a lot of pain and unsteady on her feet. They get back to the room, talking positively about the next steps and the glimmer of light. Could the experts be wrong? Could they have been too pessimist, and the twins will pull through and the brain injury is only slight? Thoughts run through there enthusiastic minds – they could be taking home another Jake and Megan. What does a brain-injured child look like anyway? The twins look a little bruised and swollen but they could be fine, couldn't they? Ben and Lou talk about all the scenarios.

A few hours pass, they snooze, they chat, they smile and scroll, texting all the family of the next steps. A few messages come back from family and friends.

'There you go told you Hun' xx

'They will be fine'? xx

'The doctors just give you the worst-case scenario, stay strong they will be fine'. xx

'Such great news, can't wait to meet the twins'?

'Stay strong Hun, thinking of you both'!

'Thinking of you all' x

'Keep in touch, love to all'.

Ben looks at the messages and wants to believe that all

will be well, and the doctors were wrong but had that nagging doubt that this wasn't the case.

Mid-afternoon, their silence is broken by the lovely Róisín. Róisín explains that Holly had her intubation tube removed and was breathing alone. Lou and Ben hug and kiss each other in relief and delight. This was an amazing step for the couple and more importantly for Holly. With a spring in their steps, they followed Róisín to the twin's incubator and look at the precious bundle breathing for herself, still with nasal gastric tube connected and monitor on her toe but she was free to breath. Róisín asked if they wanted to hold Holly and with a tear Lou jumps at the chance to hold her breathing. As Holly is passed over, her eyelids flicker and her dark eyes can be seen. A blank expression comes across Holly's traumatised face. The trauma of being starved for thirty minutes is a start straight out of the gates of hell for one so small and precious. Lou gazes down, a proud mother staring into the soul of her precious daughter wanting to fix everything. They share a beautiful but brief moment together and then Lou looks at Ben and asks if he wants to hold his daughter. Ben with no tears left jumps at the chance and sits down in the large, padded hospital chair. With a beaming smile he holds out his huge arms to the precious bundle. Holly's expressionless face looks up but through him. The nurses then insist that Holly is placed back into her cot and commence feeding her through the nasal gastric tube. As the precious bundle is lifted back into her cot, Ben and Lou's gaze turns to Teddy. Ted is still really unwell and struggling to fight to get off the seizure medication. Ben and Lou both pull their hands to their mouths and blow a kiss, touching Teddy's Perspex incubator willing him to fight to get the next stage.

The following days are a 'rinse and repeat', holding Holly and watching Teddy through the Perspex, changing his teddies. On day two, they receive the news they have been waiting for; Ted is off the seizure medication and responding well. The next day the team will attempt to remove the intubation tube.

Ben and Lou can see light at the end of the tunnel and are counting down the hours now until this happens, and they can hold a breathing, Teddy.

Overnight, Ted's epilepsy drugs are reduced to see how he reacts, and he relapses, so they are increased again. Ted has been through quite a birthing ordeal and his head severely swollen and bruised. Ted's eyes are still tightly shut, and his face resembles a boxer in the twelfth round.

The following days then follow a similar pattern going to see the twins and holding Holly who was improving every day. Ted had made it through the night epilepsy drug free and no convulsions and the removal of the invasive intubation tube. Ben and Lou then had the chance to hold both twins. It was a magical moment both parents holding both twins at the same time. Many photos were taken of the smiling parents holding both twins. This wasn't even base camp though on the mountain they had to climb, base camp was leaving the hospital to go home.

As the joy of the photo session dissipates, the couple go back to the room. Ben slips out to get a brew with a huge grin on his face, Róisín walks back with Ben to the room to talk them through the next steps. This is the news they have been waiting for, Róisín explains they are going to the new mums' suite. The suite was set up away from the noise of the ward, visitors, and babies. It was set up as a medical room with costs and a double bed. The parents would remain there with the support of the nursing staff until they leave for good. Ben and Lou were nervous but beaming, this was amazing news. The babies would be moved from the ICU unit to the room later today. The hospital was desperate for space and wanted to expedite that move. Ben and Lou jump on their phones when Róisín leaves and text the world, they wanted to broadcast the news. Ben had recently posted the picture of the four of them with a massive response. This was well worth broadcasting to all the groups they were in, family and friends. It was an amazing moment and the couple started to prepare the room, the twins clothing and are just over the moon to all be in the same room.

As they sit on the end of the bed, Róisín comes in followed by a gaggle of nurses and most importantly the twins in there Perspex homes. This time the couple's tears are of joy and happiness. The handover then begins, and they are settled in along with their gastro pump feeds, monitors and equipment. All put into position for night one – and so it begins.

Ben and Lou, stare at the twins. Two miracles laid right there who have survived such trauma. Róisín comes to check on the couple who explain they will be looked after 24/7 by the nursing team who are outside, and they will do regular observations and medical checks. As the settle down for the night, Lou leaves the bedside light on and cannot go straight to sleep, Ben on the other hand is out like a light while Lou is still whispering to him. Lou sleeps with one eye open, upright, and still with a little smile on her face. The nurses check the twins through the night who, still on their feed pumps, are well fed but cry for nappy changes. This is good sign.

The next day, various specialists arrive to check on the twins, Ophthalmologists, Sensory, Ear, Nose and Throat specialists and Neuro specialists. It's a constant procession followed by a paediatrician who explains they will be going separately for brain scans and one of the parents can go with each. This will give a detailed scan of where the damage has occurred, crucial for understanding future prospects for the twins.

As they are taken down separately the twins behave brilliantly, and they are able to get a really clear picture of the brains. In the next twenty-four hours the couple will know with very little amount of certainty the future prospects for their precious bundles of joy.

The next day they are with the twins, working with the sensory playworker with special needs toys to stimulate the twins. Lou had been expressing ready for this afternoon which was a chance to see if the twins would ever feed orally. As they are playing, a new doctor comes in with a brown envelope. He introduces himself and asks if they could sit down to go through the brain scan results. The doctor holds up the scan and starts to point at the Magnetic Resonance Image (MRI scans) he has in his hand, shuffling through the sets. Ben and Lou are hanging on his every word.

'We can see from the scans that there is extensive damage to the basal ganglia. This area lies deep within the brain and are involved in a wide range of processes such as emotion, reward processing, habit formation, movement, and learning. It is heavily responsible for co-ordinating sequences such as motor activity you would use when playing a musical instrument, playing football, dancing, or playing tennis,' the doctor says.

'I can see here damage the cerebellum, a separate structure located at the rear base of the brain, really important for fine motor control, the type that allows us to use a pen or a knife and fork. It controls things like our fixed gaze on a location as we rotate our heads.

'Prefrontal cortex (PFC) is here, and this is part of the neocortex that sits at the very front of the brain.

'It helps us with many complex cognitive functions. It also helps us hold information in our short-term memory.

'This here is the hippocampus, located in the brain's temporal lobe. This is where episodic memories are formed and indexed for later access. Episodic memories are autobiographical memories from specific events in our lives, like the cup of tea we had with a friend last week or the chats we had with friends.

'There is also damage to the neocortex. The Neocortex is for the higher functions such as sensory perception, generation of motor commands, spatial reasoning, and language. And the Amygdala. This is particularly important for strong emotional memories. Things like shame, joy, love, or grief

'The damage is wide ranging and the effects of this won't be known for some time. Your doctor will discuss all of this with you back at Nottingham and put you in touch with the specialists. Both scans are showing more or less the same damage with slight variation.'

The parents, not open mouthed, but as good, are trying to understand what on earth is going on and what the doctor has just articulated.

'Do you have any questions?' he finishes.

The couple ask again, 'what does this mean in the long term?'

The doctor is done, he has delivered his news and expresses again that Nottingham will answer any questions. He packs his scans away and shuffles his way out of the room, wishing the parents all the very best for the future.

The parents sit on the bed and discuss what they have been told. It's a body blow as they were both on the up. Then the reassuring Róisín enters the room, and they talk about what they have just been told. Róisín tries to raise the mood in the room and switch gear. They now look at giving the babies their first oral feed. This distracts the parents who get Holly ready for her first taste of mums breast milk.

Róisín then brings over a bottle with a range of teat ends to test to get the right flow. Holly has a very slow suck reflex due to the brain damage called neurogenic dysphagia. As they bring the teat to Holly's mouth, she cannot take the flow, so they reduce the flow of the teat. This is so slow that hardly any milk comes out, so Róisín gets her scissor out and cuts a small slit in the top of teat. After about thirty seconds, a small air bubble pops up into the bottle and Holly takes her first oral fluid. It's a triumph and against the experts' opinion. They repeat with Ted with the same result, it takes a little bit longer, but he does it. A small bubble pops into the bottle and Ted is on his way to drinking and eating. Over the coming days, they repeat this 3-4 times a day and one bubble becomes two, becomes three to a full quarter of a bottle. It's miraculous and Róisín is over the moon for the family. Then comes a test with food and the twins fight to eat and drink the doctors and nurses are astounded. This is the best possible start for the twins, taking oral food and drink will give them an amazing start. As the food and drink amounts increase, there is talk of removing the nasogastric tubes. Amazing progress and such great news for the family, as this will expedite getting the children home.

Over the days the twins make huge progress with the feeding, seizures do not return, and they can actually talk about going home. Lou is feeling better and stronger every day.

Then the day comes. Leaving the sanctuary and security of this room with the support network home, only one hundred and ten miles away but worlds away. The 'what if's start; what if the kids are ill, what if they need a nurse, will they have to go back where this all began?

The chance to have the family back together though would be amazing. Back with Jake and Megan who could help look after them and get to know their new brother and sister.

This is it. The family are being discharged and back under the care of Nottingham hospital, back to West Bridgford to their beloved family home. The team go through the checklist and bring in a huge number of medical supplies. Ben is sent to the car to get the car seats to secure the twins in the car. The parents start the many journeys to and from the car with the boxes, bags, and equipment. The car is crammed with the exception of two spaces for the twins. The goodbyes start along with tears, thank you's and cards for the staff. It's a momentous and scary moment for Ben and Lou. The twins are oblivious, wrapped up tight in their blankets and woolly hats. The children are safely fixed in the back seat, Ben, and Lou glance back and see their two scrappers, against all the odds they are going home. They stick on the radio crank up the Stone Roses - I am The Resurrection with huge grins on their face start the journey back to Nottingham in the sunshine. As they pass the signs for Manchester, they grab a Starbucks before they hit the Peak District, skirt around Sheffield and down the M1 where they start to see the signs for Nottingham. There is now a quiet hush in the car, twins asleep and two very nervous parents and the emotion is building as they pull off the M1 back to their home. They pass the hospital where it all happened and there is silence as they anticipate seeing Jake and Megan. They have asked that no one is at home while they get themselves together and get the twins settled, no fanfare, no banners, nothing. As they pull up to the house, they bring the car to a standstill and check in on each other and carry the twins into the house and welcome them to their new home.

It's slow, it's emotional and not the fairy-tale. Ben starts bringing in the supplies and equipment, one run after another piling onto the island where once sat the champagne and canopies. Now it looks like a hospital ward supplies cupboard. Lou sets about feeding and changing whilst Ben uploads the overnight bags and dustbin bags of washing. Felicity had left the house immaculate, piling up the ironed washing and the kitchen had been left spotless. Ben gets a brew on, and Lou starts to separate the whites and coloureds for the washing machine. The twins are perched on the settee and are never left out of sight.

The front door then barrels open and Megan and Jake pile in. Hugs and kisses all round from mum and dad. Felicity and Henry stand well back and leave this magical reunion to play out. Lou cannot let go of her two olden children and then Ben comes in for a four-way hug. As they separate, Megan and Jake walk over to Ted and Holly who are still fast asleep. They stroke the blankets and Lou introduces their new brother and sister. So many questions from two so young, to them both they just look like two normal babies, two normal siblings, a new brother and sister. They have a lovely moment together and then Felicity and Henry walk in and then Lou breaks down. Ben holds Jake and Megan and lets Lou have her moment to let it all out. Ben takes Jake and Megan in the garden to let Lou talk through what they know so far. Ben gives it sometime as this will be one of many explanations without any certainty or definitive end. As he comes in, they all hug and Felicity reassuring says to Jake and Megan, 'Isn't it wonderful to have your new brother and sister back?'

Ben's gut feeling is, this is just the start and there will be no fairy-tale ending.

Chapter 5

We Want Answers

Deadline day has arrived. Following a letter shortly after Ben and Lou arrived home with the twins, they had been invited back into to see the original doctor; Dr Vaughan, to discuss the traumatic birth night. It was opening a Pandora's box of emotion. They had met Dr Vaughan who had accessed and created the birthing plan with them both, adding risks and protocol for the team when they arrived.

Following Megan's caesarean, they discussed at length the risk, the fact they were expecting twins and the need for the birth to be carefully managed.

Ben and Lou load the twins into their car seats and start the journey back to the hospital. Lou felt angry, sick, and anxious having to go back to the place where this nightmare had unfolded. Not a word is spoken, Lou is looking out of the window – one of their favourite songs is on the radio – 'Sally Cinnamon' by Stone Roses from back in the day. Lou always used to sing to Ben jokingly that 'you are my world 'and Ben would sing the line back 'you taste of cherryade'. It seems a million miles away from where they are now – the song plays with just a glance from Lou. She is hurting and the anxiety is palpable in the car. Holly's is grumbling, Ted's looks out of the window at the passing buildings.

As they drive into the hospital entrance, Ben bites his lip, gripping the steering wheel. He is caught between not breaking down or blowing out with a stream of frustrated 'fuck's. He needs to be strong and stick to his line of questioning to out the truth. Knowing he needs to be strong; Ben slips his hand over to Lou's knee. She is motionless, and they pull into a parking space she moves his hand off her knee and turns to the children who are oblivious to what's about to be said by the man in charge.

Ben jokes to Lou, "Here goes £20 on parking, £20 for the privilege of listening to what went wrong eh'!"

Lou just mutters something extremely quietly back.

"Lou, are you ok?"

"Let's just get this done," she says darkly.

They step out of the car, unclip the car seats and put the seats into the twin's buggy frame and get them comfy. The day is cloudy, and rain is in the air – it sums up their mood as they load up their rucksacks full of feed, toys to distract and changing gear. They push the babies towards hospital from the car park, passing happy parents looking lovingly down at their bundles of joy. Lou glazes over, focusing on the horizon, just pushing the buggy emotionless through the passing people, using it as a battering ram, no smiles. She's like Richard Ashcroft in the 'Bittersweet Symphony' video, people avoiding the incoming buggy and determined and backpacked parents walking at pace.

As they walk towards the main entrance Ben notices patients dressed in fluffy slippers, cheap dressing downs, tattoos, and dry skin nattering away at the hospital door. Most smoking, some ironically on drips. Ben start replaying The Editors' song in his head 'Smokers at the hospital door' to himself walking behind the buggy and Lou as it parts the oncoming people.

Ben takes a deep breath as they cross the threshold and work their way through to reception, looking up for the signs to get to the right department. As they take a turn down another long corridor, Ben's stomach tightens, and it feels like he is going to a job interview. He takes the lead in front of the buggy and turns back to see the twins staring through the blinks up at the fluorescent tubes down through into the deepest depths of the hospital. As Ben stops to look for the right sign, Lou rams into Ben. He turns to her, knowing he cannot drop the F-bomb.

"Sorry Ben. Are you OK?" Lou asks.

Ben holds in the fucks, rubbing the back of his now reddening Achilles.

This unsettles the twins, and they start to get cranky as they complete the final leg of the march to the right place. Lou pacifies them while Ben leads the way again, biting his lip and , overdoing it a little, starts to limp slightly as he keeps looking back to ensure Lou doesn't wipe him out completely.

They get closer to the end point, through endless dimly lit corridors, past the hard-working staff and concerned relatives walking to and from the wards. Ben notices that the hospital looks tired, with buckets for the dripping water from broken water pipes, lino peeling and battered walkways. It smells of carbolic soap, bleach, and damp walls.

Ben pushes open the double doors to the maternity unit and walks up to reception. He snaps at the receptionist, asking for the directions to Dr Vaughan's office.

The receptionist explains that it is round the corner and they will let Dr Vaughan know they are here, and they can wait to be called. As they cross the maternity area with expectant mothers and ecstatic new mums and dads, both parents' bodies are taught.

It's torture. All Ben wants to do is stand on chair and warn the whole room of the dangers of the 'best moment of their life'; *here's my checklist before you hand over your life to these so professionals!* Ben keeps these thoughts contained.

Lou is holding back her searing anxiety and is very apprehensive of what's to follow.

They sit at the back of the room and pacify the children with their sensory toys. Ben and Lou just want to keep themselves to themselves. The room is busy and noisy with a few of the babies screaming waiting for their check-ups.

To their horror, a couple come over to them. It's an expectant mother who has been pacing the room in discomfort joined by her partner.

"Hi. Twins, that's amazing!" the expectant mother says.

"Yes," both parents mutter quietly.

"How are they doing?" she continues.

"Er, yes fine thanks..." Ben answers awkwardly.

"What's their names?"

"Ted and Holly."

"Aww, lovely names," she gushes.

The expectant parents delve into a diatribe about who they are and how excited they are about the impending birth. Something about clothing brands, organic food, hippy parenting, Buddhism, and fucking Montessori pre-schools. Ben stares back in complete amazement; Lou looks at the mother then completely ignores them both and stays focused on the twins.

"Anyway, all the best with the twins," the expectant mother says finally, smiling.

Lou smiles back, Ben smiles sarcastically back with a 'thanks, you to'.

They are completely oblivious, smile and wander back over to the other side of the room in their fucking dungarees and hemp sweater. Ben wants to tell them to 'fuck off' and is thinking, *get us out of this torture chamber of expectation and happiness.*

Ben turns to Lou and mutters, 'fuck this.' He gets up and goes to the reception. Two young nurses are leaning over the desk talking to the receptionist. As one of the young nurses looks back with a smile, Ben transforms from angry and impatient to flirty and cheery. The nurse's beautiful smile, deep green eyes, and immaculate complexion change Ben momentarily and he smiles and flirts for a moment. The receptionist notices this and asks if she can help.

"Oh, yes, sorry. We have been waiting for a while and wondered if we would be much longer?" Ben glances at the nurses who are looking through some notes on the desk and trying to work.

"Won't be long now, if you take a seat the doctor will call you." The receptionist smiles.

"Oh, thanks."

Ben hangs around the desk making small talk with both nurses. From across the room, Lou clocks it and stares at cheery, fun Ben. His behaviour really fucks her off. The nurses now have what they need but Ben is holding them both with his chatter. The nurses are keen to get to their patients and close Ben down who watches them both walk off and then, as if coming out or trance, turns to Lou and his children. Ben sits down next to Lou with a smile. Finally, after 20 minutes they are called into to see the doctor with all the answers. Ben's smile disappears and they get their kit together and wheel the buggy to where the nurse is waiting to guide them in.

They open the door to a room with no windows, like a prison cell. Papers piled high with tired filing cabinets and threadbare chair. Old school examination certificates are proudly displayed on the wall with various trophies piled on the shelves.

Dr Vaughan is an experienced doctor from a long line of doctors in his family and there are pictures of his family line next to pictures of him at some shoot or other, holding a dead pheasant.

"Good morning to you both!" Dr Vaughan greets them. "How are things?"

"As you can imagine, they are not great, " Ben growls.

"Ok, let's see what the notes say." Dr Vaughan drops his glasses on a chain from round his neck to the tip of his nose.

Ben throws Lou a single look that says, 'are you telling you haven't even read the fucking notes? A few seconds pass that feel like hours as Dr Vaughan goes through the notes with his hand on his chin – rubbing it furiously looking for the words.

"Ok, the twins appear to have suffered extensive brain damage due to hypoxia, sometimes referred to as birth Asphyxia. Yes, it was all very sudden."

"What does that mean for the twins?" Ben asks.

Dr Vaughan carries on reading the notes.

"Well, it's really hard to say at this point. Extensive motor development delays and I can see early indications that there is severe damage to parts of their brains. You are due some more extensive scans shortly, are you not?"

"Yes, we have an appointment."

"How old are they now?"

"Six weeks."

"Six weeks. And what has the paediatrician said?" asks Dr Vaughan.

"The damage is extensive, but they cannot give us the long-term outcomes yet as it's too early and they need to do more brain scans," Ben reports.

"Sure, sure, ok. The outcome may well be Cerebral Palsy but it's hard to say and Cerebral Palsy has so many outcomes. So, it's a very worrying business, isn't it?"

"That's an understatement, Dr Vaughan," Ben says.

"And how are they both behaving now?"

"Very unsettled and really, really hard to get off to sleep, both the same really. They wake in the night for feeds, and they take a lot of getting off again."

Smirking, Dr Vaughan states, "It was all a bit of a situation really all night wasn't it. How are you both coping it must have been tough?"

"It's been really, really hard, YES," Lou says, barely able to keep her temper.

"Did the paediatricians say any more when you spoke to them?"

"They did say it was a lack of blood and oxygen to the brains and the outcome will be a version of Cerebral Palsy, but they couldn't say how bad it will be."

"Why were they not delivered quicker?" Lou demands.

"Ok, looks like things happened very fast," Dr Vaughan says.

Ben thinks *Fast. You twat. Is that not how birth happens at the end?*

Instead, he asks out loud, "'Things seemed to happen very quickly,' what does that mean?"

While Lou asks, "Why did this happen? The twins were fine all the way through, why, doctor, did they arrive brain damaged?

"Let me see," Dr Vaughan ponders. "You were monitored, and you called for help, is that right?"

"Yes. Why did I not get pain relief to do an emergency caesarean?" Lou asks the question that has been plaguing her for weeks.

"It was too late for the pain relief to be administered for the caesarean." Reading through his glasses on the end of his nose Vaughan just says again, "Yes, you didn't have time for that did you....Erm..."

"No, we know that. But, why?"

"It was all a bit of a bad business, wasn't it?"

Ben is sitting on his hands, seething, desperate to maul Vaughan for his object arrogance.

"Why did the midwife keep disappearing off to other rooms?" Lou asks.

"Yes, they were very busy that night!" Dr Vaughan says.

"They were. But they knew the twins were coming, didn't they?"

"From the notes it looks like the midwife called the registrar who was busy and the SHO came to assist."

"SHO, what is that?" Lou asks.

"Senior house officer who was on duty," Dr Vaughan explains. "Dr Paninakis then came."

"Yes, but not straight away though," Lou says, exasperated.

'Ah yes there were a few minutes gap, I can see that." Vaughan says arrogantly and defensively. "She seemed to have a little difficulty didn't she."

"Not just a little, Doctor, we think a lot!" Lou says. "Why did that happen? Is the SHO qualified and why did they not ask for help?"

"The Senior House Officer is a very high level of doctor and Dr Paninakis is a very, very competent under the registrar – Dr Randrani."

"The Doctor who delivered the twins in the end."

"Yes, it seems you couldn't tolerate the cup that Dr Paninakis tried, so a little pain relief was administered around the opening."

"Yes, she couldn't find the right size cup or something!"

"I mean, it all happened in about 10 minutes must have seemed like a lifetime to you both," Dr Vaughan says.

"Yeah, it did."

"And of course, because it all happened so quickly and there was no time to give you an epidural for the delivery as would have been the normal course of action. The babies couldn't tolerate the cup if they could of you wouldn't have needed so much anaesthetic."

"What does that mean?" Lou asks.

"So, she did manage to use the forceps, she did actually use the forceps for deliver, I think, didn't she?"

"No, Doctor, she tried and failed then the registrar had to be called. There was a delay as the SHO wouldn't let them call him. When the midwife did, the SHO made it clear that she was not happy with the midwives as they had stopped listening to her instructions."

Dr Vaughan shifts uncomfortably in his chair. Ben and Lou got the feeling that this was not the first time Dr Paninakis has been called into question.

"Ah, and then I read here there was a clot behind the afterbirth."

“What does that mean?”

“They call it an ‘abruptio placentae’ which means the placenta breaks away from the wall of the womb and that’s probably why the heart rate went down.”

“Why weren’t things escalated quicker and why wasn’t Dr Randrani called earlier?” Lou asks, getting tired of the Latin words and medical terms.

“Erm, let me see. It was a very busy night on the ward, and I can see he was called.”

“Yes, but that was when the twins were in distress, the heart monitor thing was very slow and sometimes was making a noise and sometimes it wasn’t.”

Vaughan continues to read on, rubbing his chin, clearly wishing a hole would swallow him up. “Yes, well it was all very quick, but it would appear that Dr Randrani did all he could to expedite the twin’s delivery.’

‘Yes, but by that point it was too late, and the damage was done, right?’

‘Er, it’s hard to tell really.’

‘What do you mean, hard?’

‘It appears to just be one of those things really. There can be some serious, very serious bleeding under those circumstance.’

‘What circumstances?’

‘It can happen when you go into labour and of course that can be disastrous, because the afterbirth comes adrift and of course the babies cannot survive.’

‘But they did?’

‘Yes, yes so obviously this was the cause and the twins started to show sudden signs of distress with a very low heart rate and that was the first clue in all of this.’

‘But it was almost half an hour ? Why?’

‘Yes, yes, it’s very, very difficult in these circumstances and as I say this is what happened and why the afterbirth came adrift. It’s difficult to say really, yes, you know the whole labour was very quick.’

‘But half an hour is a long time!’

'I mean how long were you in labour for,' Dr Vaughan says.

'8 hours?'

'And at the end it was all very quick, wasn't it? Quite a business.'

'Yes, very quick. I dilated very quickly.' Lou says.

'And when you were at 5cm, you didn't feel the need for the epidural?'

'I was in a lot of pain, the midwife said she wanted to go through the protocol as she was new to the ward and just finished her training and go through the process as per her training.'

'The midwife was Sally. Sally Warbouys, is that correct?'

Lou nodded. 'I explained I was in a lot of pain and said it wasn't working so to use the TEN's machine.'

'You asked for the TEN's machine.'

'No. No, I didn't!' Lou says. 'Sally said she wanted to start it off naturally with a TEN's machine. The TEN's machine didn't work either and I explained that I was still in a lot of pain.'

'There must have been desperate concern for the babies and there was certainly no time to give you a spinal or an epidural anaesthetic. It seems Sally did what was quickest rather than call for the spinal to be administered or to do an emergency caesarean section, you see. You had had a previous caesarean, is that right?'

'Yes, I did.'

'But you were insistent on a normal delivery, is that right?'

'Yes, but I was high risk, wasn't I? Why wasn't I encouraged to get the emergency option in place so we could get the babies out quickly if needed?'

Silence falls over the conversation.

Dr Vaughan speaks again, 'The delivery was all going to plan, and the first stage was 3 hours, you know as they calculate it, the second stage was hastened but it was only 31 minutes in total so just under 4 hours. From your notes, the last baby was breach, is that right?'

'Yes, extended breach!'

'And you opted for an elective caesarean, didn't you?'

'Yes.'

'So, you have never had a labour before.'

'Yes, I had Jake.'

'It was a pretty quick labour.'

'I had been induced though which speeds things up doesn't it?'

'No, not really, being induced should lengthen labour in my professional opinion.'

'That's not what they have been told and with Jake they were told they were giving it to me to speed it up.'

'Erm, but I think there was for some reason or other an issue but, we will never know, because they don't know when the afterbirth comes away which it can do in very, very rare cases. It can be associated with blood pressure sometimes, before labour, that's obviously why the babies suddenly got distressed, and the heart rate started to drop. All was well and then it dropped and of course then all hell let loose. At that stage, it's very difficult for you to get the adequate pain relief you need. It's a problem because obviously the concern is to get the babies out as soon as possible, it just compounded the distress for you, I am sure.'

'Dr Randrani asked if the pelvis had been x-rayed before the delivery, have the hospital missed something?' Lou asks, remembering the nightmare night.

'No, no, no. I wouldn't have thought that with this sort of labour that would happen. It would be most irregular for that to happen,' Dr Vaughan blusters.

'But it would have helped?'

'In my professional opinion, I don't think an x-ray would have helped at this stage as things just happened so quickly at the end.'

'All the staff were talking among themselves and then asking questions of us, and the X-ray sounded like it was a big thing?' Lou presses.

'Er, no, I really don't think so, are you planning any more

children? It may be worth doing if you plan any more.'

'So, it would be helpful?' Perhaps Lou was finally getting somewhere, nailing Dr Vaughan to the wall.

'If you had particularly big twins, then it may have been relevant but in the circumstances, I don't think it would be helpful but worth doing if you do proceed with more children. I would definitely opt for a caesarean next time.'

'But that doesn't help us now, does it?!' Lou shouts.

'No, I would definitely advise a caesarean next time or at the very least get the spinal in place so they can get the baby out very quickly to avoid this unnecessary business!'

Unnecessary business! Ben and Lou exchange a look that says, WTF!! The babies are now restless and need a feed and to get out of this oppressive tomb.

'I have to say I am not a great enthusiast of the TENS machine. I mean, people talk about it a lot, but when a patient asks me about TENS, you know, I say that if you want my honest opinion, it's for the birds frankly. I mean it's good occupational therapy, and it's good for chronic back pain, it's used a lot in chronic back pain clinics, but for the pain of labour you need pain relief. It's not enough.'

'I did say when I came in that I wanted a spinal injection in case I needed a C-section,' Lou says.

'Yes, yes that's right you did. I can see that in your birthing plan, it would have made you a lot more comfortable wouldn't it.'

'Yes, but it would have meant I could have had an emergency C-section.'

'I can see that the first midwife read the birthing plans. I know, it did say what you required. Obviously when you first started having niggles, she decided to start with the TENs in a natural sort of way and see how you go. Then the first midwife that had been with you, she left right at the last minute, there was a shift change and somebody else came on.'

'Sally.'

'Yes, Sally.'

‘Right, I think as far as the little ones are concerned, it’s a question of just seeing how things go. They can’t give you chapter and verse can they. We all just need to see how it will be at this stage. I think they’re just going to see how they develop Its just a very worrying time for you. Have you had a period yet?’

‘No, because I’ve been expressing.’

‘So, the twins are having breast milk?’

‘Yes.’

‘And have the breasts settled down?’

‘Not bad, but very sore.’ Lou says. ‘Dr Randrani came to see me in the afternoon, all very upset, after it had happened, the team were all very upset.’

‘What time was the delivery?’ Dr Vaughan asks.

‘2.47am.’

‘Ah right, the graveyard shift as we call it. It can really catch us out at that time of night.’

Blank faces just stare back at the Doctor.

‘I said to them all to write a full report as to what has happened, they were all quite upset about it too, because it all hits, it hits you straight between the eyes, you know, from our point of view.’

‘If they had have done more quicker, we wouldn’t be here now, would we doctor? But they will just have to live with this on their consciences.’

Vaughan looks ruffled and starts to stutter out his words, ‘The midwife was very upset. You know these things happen, you go along, you sail along for weeks on end and months on end without a problem and then ‘bang’ suddenly you get a problem, it can be quite stressful, so as I say, I think they’ll just have to live with this. How’s your tail end now?’

‘Still very tender and struggling to walk long distances.’

‘I don’t really think there is any more I can say at this stage, and you are in good hands, I think they just have to hope that things work out and see how things develop. Let’s continue the current programme of tests and checks and see how they go, it's just a great worry, I know. It will get better and better. I think the reason why it happened, you can never be sure about these things, but it looks very much as though it was because the afterbirth. Part of it came adrift and the babies got distressed, I'm just sorry you hadn't had your epidural before the event, you know. I usually say to folk if they're going to have an epidural, have your epidural as soon as your labour's established, as soon as you know it's an ongoing business, even if it does seem to be a bit early in the day because you never quite know what's going to happen. Obviously, you got on very quickly from 5cms and I think it caught them out a little bit, just made it worse. They did put local anaesthetic around the outside for the Ventouse then put in the spinal block. The problem is, of course, it always takes time for the nerve blocks to work. I think sometimes what happens, particularly in the panic to get the baby out, the block goes in, and the forceps go on, and the baby's delivered really almost before the block becomes fully affected, pretty horrendous for you. OK, we just have to hope it all works out.'

'Were mistakes made?' Lou demands.

'I think the team did all they could under the circumstances and the Incident Investigation report they all completed just showed they did everything could within the timescales. I was as keen as you to get to the bottom of this but overall, incredibly proud of what the team achieved under the circumstances in such a short period of time,' Dr Vaughan says. 'I think we should all just give it time and get through the next few weeks and see how they go. Now you both take care please and all the very, very best.'

As Vaughan holds up the paper file and bangs it shut on the desk, Ben and Lou are perplexed. They look at each other. No answers, nothing but patronising excuses. 30 minutes of incompetence and a family's life changed forever, explained within another 30 minutes by a doctor covering his arse. They are fuming.

Walking back through the maternity reception, Ben turns

to Lou. 'Arrogant twat.'

'Ben, that isn't helping.' Lou sighs.

'What the fuck were they going on about? This is a cover up and they are covering their arse. Something's not right. There's no way those times he said make any sense.'

As they walk down the corridors again, they pass the entrance to the children's ward Lou lets Ben knows she needs a wee. Ben stops opposite a waiting area for what must be the children's cancer ward. Young children and adolescent patients walk by with nurses clinging on to their drips, no hair from the chemotherapy. Their blue gowns flap at the bottom, touching their slippers as they Shuffle from one test or scan to another. This is poignant moment for Ben as although not the same condition as what the twins have, the future they are facing is very much aligned.

Ben has a sinking feeling. Having never been exposed to tragedy, illness, or potential death, he was a in a new world of emotions. What is unfolding before his eyes is the reality of other people's lives, it's all around him. Not the perfect middle-class lives of his friends and family, but another life; real life.

The kind of lives of working and the lower classes are more likely to observe on a daily basis, poor health, and disability. The life where cash and opportunity are key, magnifying what comes with ill health and private healthcare and access to medical help. Ben realises that there is a world totality reliant on the NHS, a world that is totally alien to Ben and his cohort who, if cannot they get it pay for it. The suffocating air of smugness and comfort of wealth that engulfs the middle and upper classes who would never expect to be mixing on hospital wards and expect hotel-style accommodation and privacy.

Although money can mitigate risk or buy healthcare when having a baby with the NHS, Ben now knows that all are throwing the white ball down onto the roulette wheel and sometimes it can land on green, changing the course of the lives of families. Entering the maternity ward for that moment, the middle and upper classes put their lives and those of their children in the same hands as any class and sometimes it doesn't go to plan. It's one of life's levellers.

These children are resilient and have enthusiastic smiles in the face of what Ben thinks could be leukaemia and cancer, all at various stages – some in wheelchairs and some being moved around in beds. In the five minutes waiting for Lou, this is a humbling and heart wrenching experience. As the doors open opposite, Ben can see down the ward with beds full of the young facing nurses and worried parents. All working through their own battles and challenges. Externally Ben was a brash, confident go-getter, under this brash exterior Ben was deeply flawed and incredibly insecure.

His weakness was always to go off the deep end and would result in spending, gambling or into the arms of another – craving affection and affirmation. This was his escape route and what he saw in those moments would only exacerbate those cravings to escape.

As they walk out of the hospital, Ben is silenced by what he has seen but, furious at Dr Vaughan's explanations of the events of the night and the Trust's explanations. They walk out of the hospital entrance, past the choking fumes of the Benson and Hedges and Vape clouds to the car park and back to the car.

The battle is not over, Ben wants to come out fighting. Lou wants to know what's next and what she can do for the twins to maximise their future. As they pull out of the hospital back to the sanctuary of home, the front seats are totally silent, the back seat is a cacophony of cries and whimpers.

The battle has begun for answers and the future prospects of the twins.

Chapter 6

Showing Your Hand Too Early

It just never sat right. The meeting with Vaughan, closed meetings, and the lack of written response. Where did the actual notes go? The notes with crossed-out lines, times changed and some completely rewritten.

That night was a disaster, and Ben and Lou knew it. Since the birth of the twins Ben and Lou wanted to see the actual notes as what they were sure was 25 minutes had now been reduced to 10 minutes. How was this possible? There is no way it was 10 minutes. Where are the notes from the night, showing the disaster unfolding and why do they all now match perfectly? Ben and Lou needed to break down the clandestine organisation and get to the truth. They couldn't do it alone they needed help.

Ben and Lou got some legal advice back after they were suspicious about the cover up. A recent case had been in the local paper and the child had been compensated, the financial settlement had stuck in Ben's mind rather than the case. The couple had been fighting for 10 years for justice, so time was of the essence in Ben's mind.

Ben had an old school mate who had a local solicitor's firm. Ben reached out to his old acquaintance, Vikesh. Vikesh was incredibly bright, and his speciality was property and land law, but his practice had jumped onto the ambulance-chasing bandwagon with some success. Vikesh sniffed out 'no win no fee' medical negligence claims and funding channels, it was very lucrative, and he linked up with specialist barristers up and down the country. Once on the circuit it was a bit of a gravy train.

He had the contacts needed and this would be a great step up as the claims value were rising exponentially. Vikesh had had some success, but only with low-level claims that were sure things. Brain injury medical negligence claims were different gravy and extremely complicated, but he was confident he had what he needed and a little black book of contacts. The case Ben had summarized against the trust was very strong anecdotally. Vikesh and Ben met up a follow up meet in the local boozer and, over beers, Ben laid bare what had happened and the case he had read about. Pound signs lit up in Vikesh's eyes and although he had zero specific experience in this area, he was a fake it till you made it type of guy. He assured Ben he would have a crack it and freestyled about the 'similar' cases he had won, and reeled off his barrister mates cases and the multi-million-pound claims that were in the bag. With medical negligence claims rising in value Vik's wanted this one. Vik's had brought the paperwork committing the family to his services and legal aid help. Ben signed up over a pint, confident Vik's would look after them. When he stumbled back home, smelling of stale beer, Lou was really annoyed Ben had signed up without her knowledge but that was Ben all over.

The initial meeting between Vik's, Ben and Lou was emotional. Their timings were vague as they were caught up in the moment and the meeting with Dr Vaughan gave very little away in terms of what they recollected compared to what he had down on paper from the people involved. They recollected about half an hour delay, trying hard to recall the events through the trauma and PTSD. Vik's listened intently to Ben and Lou's recollection and built out his case using the timings they sort of knew. As they completed their first couple of hours with Vik's, Lou was still unsure. Vik's let them know he would deal with this swiftly and with money on his mind, cracked on applying for further and expanded legal aid and they were off and 100% committed.

Vikesh clumsily issued instructions the very next week which alerted the Trust who immediately appointed their lawyers and a dark veil fell over the whole episode. The Trust went onto a war footing.

Signalling to the Trust they intended litigation exposed the parents and the twins. Letters passed forwards and backwards between the Trust and Vikesh's firm.

The first legal aid payments for Vikesh's time had been signed off and the payments starting to drop into his account. For the parents, it was false hope that there may be some finality, answers and, more importantly, funding to support their situation. The communication between the hospital and Vikesh continued with copies being sent to the parents. Every phone call, meeting, email, and letter was logged and billed. Ben and Lou just had to rely on their trust in Vikesh that he was doing the right thing. The message back from Vik's was always positive.

Financially they were screwed and needed legal aid and Vikesh to proceed this claim. Ben had made some really bad calls, borrowed, and leveraged against the house way beyond what they could ever support. His 'Manchester project' was the biggest issue as interim payments we overdue and missing payments wasn't an option.

All Lou could see was that the compensation would at least give the twins what they needed. However, Ben thought it was his golden egg. A chance for him to alleviate all his financial woes. The twins and their lifetime of needs was only at the back of his mind. It was all about the cash.

Every time he met with Vikesh, the solicitor's over

confidence that they were onto a winner was a little unnerving, but Ben and Lou kept going. Months would pass between letter exchanges, but the Trust was adamant at every stage that there was no case to answer, 'without prejudice'. The Trust held their line. They had obviously instructed senior barristers as William Benton at Talbert's was firing back the responses on the Trust's behalf.

Ben and Lou were asked to hospital for various appointments, brain scans and consultancies over the years. They attended as advised by Vikesh but asked not to discuss the case.

Chapter 7

In Too Deep

Still trying desperately to keep up with his friendship group who were driven by social status, competitiveness, and greed, Ben's finances spiralled. He could not be on his own he had to be around people constantly, a full diary. His weaknesses and his hidden insecurities were being massively exposed by this reckless acceleration of his own downfall and his lack of time spent with his own family.

Ben owed money all over, including his friends and family. Ben was into Ferg, his builder friend for £10,000's and Ferg knew it may not come back any day soon. He wasn't prepared to get deeper. Family houses has been re-mortgaged to release cash to reduce interest borrowing's, payments owed and investments that had on the whole gone wrong. Gambling for fun had become a serious addiction trying to cover loses with his 'system' as he called it. Ben was incredibly charming and had a way to convince people 'the next one' would be a flyer, hiding a trail of disasters behind him. If Ben needed money for the next investment or to pay off an existing debt he was like a dog with a bone and just wouldn't let it go. Friends, family, friends of friends, business colleagues were all fair game to be tapped up for cash. Ben's money merry-go-round never stopped and usually resulted in a negative, another lost friend, an aggrieved family member or the threat of violence.

Ben's biggest mistake was getting close to Uncle Frank who he looked up to as he got to know him and listen to his stories. Frank was a bit of bruiser and not cut from the same cloth as his brother, Ben's dad. Frank was always in one scrape or another but over the last 10 years a so had stepped up his game to gain legitimacy in his hometown of Manchester.

Large housing developments, Manchester bars and clubs were Uncle Frank's thing and buying up plots of industrial space or run down townhouses and turning them into student flats was how he started to make his cash and how he met his new associates who had not all made their money legitimately. The glamour around the gangster life appealed to Ben. Deep down he really wanted that 'tough guy' edge but was not really built for it. Ben had got financially deep into Frank and Co's latest project 'Manchester XS1' and committed money he didn't have on a huge development of flats on industrial land. Frank had bought in to this with a large crime family in Manchester and the payments were essential to get the project built and generating cash as required. Dates and amounts were clearly set out and, although Ben didn't have the cash, he committed 'in blood' as the returns would clear a lot of held personal debt. Ben blagged it using his charm and persuasion to get himself bought in.

Ben gambled his and his family's life with all the best intentions, clearing debt to clear up his own mess. If he couldn't pull off the 'great escape' from debt he knew the consequences, but if he couldn't meet the payments for 'Manchester XS1'the consequences were beyond any personal bankruptcy.

Over latter years, Ben had deliberately distanced himself from those he owed money to. But the helpful friends with cash had also become distant following the twin's arrival which did not help find new wells of cash to tap into.

This awkward and complicated situation affected Lou and the kids. Ben now came with a reputation, and it was well known around the old school contingent that Ben was a loose cannon with cash, and you should avoid being drawn in to his latest 'double your money' project. Once seen as a 'bit of a wide boy' Ben was now a bit of an 'ageing sad act' not to be trusted, and he knew it. The one person though that his charm was never lost on was Hetty who would forgive almost anything when it came to Ben.

Hetty and Lou were sisters but also the very best of friends growing up. Very competitive with each other which also played out with boys. The younger of the two siblings, Hetty had kept herself incredibly fit with a diet of healthy eating and the gym 5 days a week. She loved a glass of wine but preferred Vodka Martini to keep the calories low. When she wanted something or to achieve something she went straight after it, regardless of the consequences. Hetty worked hard at school and pushed herself hard backed by pushy parents. Youngest sibling syndrome drove her to achieve, and deep down she was always pushing to go beyond her friends, colleagues, and her number one target: Lou. Hetty would often talk openly about the days when she first laid eyes on Ben in a jokey but serious way. She would re-tell the story of when she and Lou met Ben and that they both had a massive crush on Ben. There was too much of an age gap at the time for Hetty to win out, and she always slightly resented the fact that she missed out. She flirted relentlessly with Ben throughout Ben and Lou's life together. Hetty was even maid of honour for Lou at the wedding. Looking back at the wedding photos, Hetty had that 'it should have been me' gaze. Ben was dashingly handsome and a real catch, all of Lou's friends would swoon in Ben's presence. As Ben and Lou embarked on married life, building a future together, Hetty drifted off into a number of relationships. Hetty did the socials but mainly hit the party and dance circuit as a single. She fuelled her energy with a blend of alcohol, ecstasy, and coke. Her lifestyle was that of a wild child and socialite, partying all night and then straight into work for 9am to hit another shift and then do it all again. Eat (a little) Sleep, Rave – Repeat. There was no such thing as a school night. Hetty saw food as a form of control and was incredibly disciplined in what she ate and what she worked off and would then binge. It was a constant battle.

While Hetty was smashing every day, burning the candle both ends, Ben and Lou were building a family. Jake and Megan came along, and Lou and Ben were the perfect new parents with a large social group through maternity groups, pre-school, and primary school. Aunty Hetty was a huge part of everything they did from a family perspective and friendship groups criss-crossed, so she socialised a lot with Ben and Lou the daylight and evening hours. As night-time fell, Ben and Hetty would disappear off and midnight onwards was Hetty's time to party.

Ben always got on well with the latest bloke that Hetty brought to the party but often wore a 'you are no threat to me and Hetty' smirk. The blokes that came back were usually devilishly handsome, but with zero personality. Hetty brought along the latest hunk as if to say to Ben they are taller, better looking, fitter than you. It was strange, almost like a sibling relationship. Lou was no longer the one to outdo in the latest test or race when it came to her men. For Hetty, it was now Ben.

Ben would flirt with other friends at parties in front of Hetty. He didn't really hide it and did like to glance of the shoulder of his latest victim to locate Hetty's gaze. He gave her an 'are you jealous?' look and gave her the eyes and a smile.

Hetty did finally settle down with one of the guys she had met, Phil, a reformed raver.

Phil was always seen as the strong and quiet one of the gang. He met Hetty quite late on after university at a local night club rave. Phil was a tall, good looking, shy gentleman. Not really into sport or the pub. More than happy looking after the house, and into walking and reading. Phil and Hetty were a very unlikely couple. Hetty dominated the relationship. They would go to raves as Phil was a poor sleeper so anything after midnight suited him and raves were their thing. Phil was quite happy ferrying Hetty and friends all over the country and driving back in the morning.

Hetty would drop Phil and move quickly onto her next victim, but Phil would always forgive her and then they would get back together. It became a pattern, always on Hetty's terms. Hetty used Phil as a fallback to fill gaps where she needed time off 'the scene' to rest, city breaks, a break from the latest frenetic relationship with a raver from the scene that she used and abused.

Phil seemed pretty happy with this and would have the odd girlfriend in between but was quite happy on his own. His character was worlds away from Ben and his friends, just a quiet raver getting on with his life building a career and always sort of know as Hetty's boyfriend or 'Booty call Phil'.

He loved to rave as he could stand at the back enjoying the music and atmosphere but didn't have to talk to anyone as the bass and persistent drumbeat drowned out all conversation. A perfect place to hide. Phil was never in the throng and was desperate to keep himself out of any limelight. Phil wasn't bothered about drinking either, just the odd ecstasy tablet or line of coke, always the nominated driver. Hetty sort of carried him and he went along with it.

Phil loved his work as a charted surveyor and his work was perfect for him – very peaceful and good for the soul. Hetty found it all incredibly dull and work was rarely discussed. He knew Hetty was too good for him, and he was batting well up the order with her. When they were out, Hetty received a lot of male and female attention, Phil knew it but, let it pass over him. Dinner parties were his biggest nightmare as there was nowhere to hide. Phil's diversion tactic was to host dinner parties at theirs as much as possible so her could be in familiar surroundings and keep away from the chat by preparing drinks or cooking dinner. All he had to do then was navigate a couple of hours at the table. By then everyone was generally pissed so didn't even notice he was there. Ben and Hetty's extreme closeness was not lost on Phil, and he always kept a watching eye over them. He knew that they had a connection and tried to keep it in check.

*

Ben and Lou had a healthy sexual relationship even after Jake and Megan but, through Lou's pregnancy with the twins, the relationship started to become non-existent, and Ben was really struggling. Ben stepped up his ' flirty Bertie' game at work and any opportunity during this time. Even though she was Lou's sister, Hetty was the main object of Ben's advances. To be around them both in a small group was incredibly intense and the connection was electric and overbearing.

This was not lost on Lou, but full days of caring for the twins meant she just couldn't be bothered to fall out with her sister. Her focus was keeping the family schedule, caring and appointments. Ben was like lost sheep with his insatiable appetite for female attention and went into overdrive. He would text Hetty which although slightly weird Hetty kind of loved, like a cheeky off-grid texting game. Always discreet and non-sexual but always checking each other out to see who will blink first.

The texts got more frequent though as Lou's pregnancy developed, and they would meet 'by chance' for coffee when diaries allowed. They talked a lot about the old days and the family dynamics. Hetty didn't want children so for Ben it was welcome respite from home stuff and particularly pregnancy and the lack of closeness with Lou.

Over the years, Hetty just passed it off and was quite happy with digital chit chat. Ben needed it to keep things going from a flirty perspective as Lou was pre-occupied with the pregnancy, the children, and then the enormity of the twins care regime. He needed his ego massaging. This carried on all the way through the pregnancy. He didn't cross any lines of acceptableness but came very close.

Chapter 8

Dinner Party Anxiety

Dinner parties were always a joy before the twins. Sharing laughs, stories and catching up on the latest celebrity and school gate gossip. Preparatory school education with Megan and Jake brought a whole new group of like-minded people into Ben and Lou's life, adding to family and friends they already had. All very similar types, driving the same cars, professional jobs, middle class, lots of disposable income, shopping, and holidaying at the same places. Carbon copies of each other and their lifestyles. Dinner parties revolved around drink, and they drank a lot – always great fun, lots of laughs. Kitchen discos were a regular event, reminiscing about the last Ibiza trip. The wine flowed as did the shots, knowing Megan and Jake were safely being looked after by the babysitters.

Lou sometimes bit her lip and felt some of the groups of friends were completely deluded about how the real world worked. Spiritual types who had never worked or had made-up jobs that weren't jobs. Part-time teaching in the evening at the local Montessori school or directors of the weird face creams, fragrance sticks, scented candles and beard oil businesses selling to mainly their like-minded friends and acquaintances. Hobbyists making no profit living off their partner's wages, inheritance, or a family trust fund. It did make Ben and Lou laugh when they would go on and on about how busy they were. Lou would often think, *come, and spend just one day in my shoes, you may think you are over-egging the term 'rushed off your feet'.*

Then there were the show-offs; new money who didn't have the gravitas or manners to pull it off and stood out like a sore thumb. After the fourth Stella or fifth glass of Chardonnay they would let their guard down and become inappropriate, aggressive, drop their R's, and generally swagger about. Lou and Ben just went along with it and would have preferred people to just be themselves. Behind their backs, the upper middle class would take the piss out of them relentlessly.

Ben was always very flirty; it was in his nature. Outgoing and confident, he loved flitting around the party talking to all the yummy mummies who loved the attention. The older females in the group knew what he was up to and laughed it off. Lou brushed off any male attention and was quite happy with her man. He was always very affectionate, caring, attentive but an absolute rogue. Lou secretly loved that as he always came back to her bed at the end of the day.

The twins changed all of that. Ben's world had been blown apart and losing 'the old Lou' had escalated his flirting from being overly friendly with someone at work to sleeping with someone from work – a younger member of staff that had taken to Ben. His constant flirting had found a victim who took pity on his situation and looked up to him and his position.

As Lou opens the mail during her morning coffee and cleaning break. She notices a printed envelope with a red stamp on the back. Lou knows exactly who this is – Tristian and Esme. Esme had created a family crest and used it to seal invites. Lou smiles, rolls her eyes, and opens the envelope. It's an expensively printed and embossed invite to a dinner party to be hosted at their new house. The invite features brochure-quality stylised images of the new gaff.

Ben and Lou's last dinner party was before the birth of the twins, so she was dreading the next one. Everything had changed, everything. Lou was fully immersed in care; Ben was struggling to find himself. Lou would quite happily respectfully decline the invitation as it was a mammoth operation to care for the twins. Ben would jump at the chance to get pissed and spend time away from the family home and be with friends – a great distraction.

Lou knew there was an absolute ton of work to put in to prepare for this one night. The twins, now 6 months old, were still getting periodic input from the local hospital. They didn't have enough health needs, though, for full funding but did tick a box due to their feeding tubes and associated care. They were deemed not quite sick enough for the real health support the family needed. Lou accepted the little they had as the team from the hospital were clinically trained.

The team at the hospital had a great relationship with the parents. The two carers they had formed a great relationship with – Dianne and Jeremy (Jez) – were always the two carers first on the list.

Dianne was amazing – worked on the wards all day and then offered an outreach service to parents like Ben and Lou. Di was joined by Jez and both trained nurses, were absolutely amazing people. Good, hard-working souls.

Lou knew they would be brilliant from the first moment they met the twins. Lou started her pre-going out list; meds prepared, beds sorted, CCTV and sound alarms checked, personal care list in place, emergency phone numbers clearly marked, location and emergency meds. The list seemed to be bloody endless. Without it though, Lou would not settle and would be reluctant to leave the house. Lou's preparation started at 3.30pm and the clock was ticking. Ben decided he was going to the rugby club to watch the local team which pissed Lou right off but, of course, Ben had a hundred reasons why it would be a good idea. *Leave it with me FFS*, Lou thought.

She actually preferred to do this alone, so it actually got done. Lou had created her own day and night care plan that had everything in. Lou expresses milk for the twins as part of the routine.

Di and Jez were due to arrive at 5pm, giving Lou an hour to get ready before they reluctantly set off to the dinner party which was starting to feel more like a job interview. Lou completes her check list, does all she can with the twins to calm them and settle them down in front of the TV. Di and Jez arrive to a warm smile from Lou, they both reassure Lou that she can get ready. 30 minutes later, Ben turns up having had more than the agreed couple of pints, ignores the twins and gives a smile and wave to Jez and Di and gets himself ready. Lou did have sympathy for Ben. She could see he was struggling and understood why he drank but felt it was selfish. At some point, he had to face this. Di and Jez were here to help, and a god send. They allowed Lou a fleeting moment of normality. Ben could show a little more respect for the job they were doing.

Megan and Jake are staying at friends, so this really helps focus Lou on the twins needs, handover and making herself look presentable.

Over the first six months of the twins' lives, Lou had realised her peer group were flaky when it really mattered.

At one really low point, her friends Lexi, Rach, Fran, sister Hetty, Joy, Esme, Cate, Joy, and Victoria really showed their true colours. Lou had been texting and WhatsApping friends trying to arrange a get together. She's had a barrage of bad news about the twins and was struggling with Megan and Jake. Ben was being distant; closeness was a thing of the past and sex was fleeting and formulaic.

After looking to fix up a date to meet up with her closest came to nothing, Lou gave up and only really saw her friends fleetingly, saying hello at the school gate was about it. Also, she no longer felt part of those virtue signalling group chats about what a great life everyone was enjoying. 'Checking in' on

Lou behind the digital curtain was way easier than having a genuine conversation, listening, and understanding the twin's daily issues. 'Hope you're ok Hun' now received a cut and paste ' yes, all good thanks' from Lou. She didn't want to bother her friends with her woes. In the beginning, she had tried to reach out with long winded 'War and Peace' texts actually detailing what had happened in her day, her worries and what her weekend looked like, but she just got one liner replies or read with no reply back. She was being ghosted by her closest friends who just could not handle her situation.

After her attempts to meet up came to nothing, she broke down outside the local pub. She'd had a really bad day after caring all day and taking the twins to meet the paediatric specialist. Knackered, she drew up to the traffic lights next to the pub. Outside, all of her friends sat laughing and joking, chatting, and enjoying a drink. The only thing missing was her. Holding back the tears, Lou pulled away from the lights and had to park up a side road. Lou was so hurt by this – they couldn't be bothered to change the time around the twins by a couple of hours. Lou missed the closeness of what she thought were her besties. The days talking about normal stuff; holidays, Housewives of Salt Lake City and making new plans. Where had this gone? Lou thought to herself. How has it come to this? Am I that shit that my besties cannot bear my company?

Lou knew that the twins and their world had come to dominate her life but surely her friends would stick by her. Digitally, superficially and from a distance was not enough to help Lou.

That sunny evening what hurt the most was the smiling and laughing faces – normal life. Almost the relief that Lou and all the baggage wasn't there, and they could talk of the normal things that Lou missed so much. Maybe this dinner party would bring the night of normality she craved.

Lou goes to the bedroom and just flops on the bed, connects her phone to the Bluetooth speaker and sticks on her sister's mix. Time on her own is rare, fully reassured her babies are ok.

She has a little sing to Kylie's Better the Devil You Know in the shower and gets herself ready as fast as possible. As she sits at the dressing table, Lou pulls at her face, thinking *God, how did I get so bloody old?* Anxiety settles in her stomach as she gets ready to meet the 'beautiful people' who will have spent all day getting ready, going to the spa, hairdresser and choosing their outfit. T hen B en a rrives, half c ut, walking into the bedroom with a bottle of beer and sits on the bed. Lou, avoiding Ben, who is divided between swigging his beer, texting, and scrolling on his phone, carries on with covering up the cracks and making herself look beautiful. Make-up hasn't been a thing for a while.

Ben's eyes don't focus. He sits on the bed and then starts getting ready slowly, no shower a quick wash down, change of shirt and done.

Lou finishes off her make-over, covering up the dark rings beneath her eyes, puts her hair up as she has not had time to get to the hairdressers for months. She puts on her favourite short top over her jeans, shakes her head in the mirror and then delves straight into the 'long list' with Di and Jez.

Getting Ted and Holly in a good place for bed was vital – Di and Jez are brilliant at the rest. They are still so young and the trauma they suffered is still ever present in their behaviour. It's in the endless hours of crying, screaming and being unsettled. There were very few smiles from the twins.

Lou and Ben had got into a routine of rocking the cots to get them off into an initial sleep, accompanied by the precious Twinkle, Twinkle Little Star wind-up lullaby nursery rhyme machine. It can take 1-2 hours a night, but it was worth it. After a full day of caring, Lou needed to get them into the initial sleep period to start the night shift. Lou's dad even helped by putting some castors on the bottom of the cots to help the rocking process.

Lou was still expressing milk for the twins, and it helped reduce the leaking. At home, the stains on her t-shirt were part of her everyday... Going into the big wide world and especially to an intimate dinner party with this particularly clean-cut, snobby group of people with lactating breasts is not a good look.

As Lou comes down, Di and Jez comment how beautiful she looks. Lou is taken a back as compliments were a rarity these days. Lou gives both Di and Jez a kiss on the cheek and thanks them both.

As Lou comes to the end of the handover, Ben is finally ready. He walks straight to the fridge and cracks open another beer. Lou mutters to herself, *looks like I am driving then – again.*

Ben walks past the care handover without a word and out to the back garden with his beer, lighting up a cigarette.

Lou is weirdly petrified about leaving the twins and being back in company. The twins have become her security blanket and she's torn between fear and excitement as this could be the start of life getting back to some sort of normality.

Lou has her usual 90's Chaf FM as they both called it on; Ben brings his bottle of beer with him. He smiles as songs from school start to play. It takes Lou right back and, for this brief moment, she feels alive. There's a sense of the lightness of normality for the first time since the twins arrived.

Just as Lou is sinking into the lightness of normality, Ben starts to list random tasks that needed doing for the twins. *You weren't even present so don't even start,* she thinks, but to keep the mood light, just ticks of the short list off verbally with a 'Yes darling, that's done, that's done.' *That's only half the list, you have no idea.*

Switching gear quickly, Lou enquires, 'How was the rugby darling?'

'Oh yes great, good catch up.' Ben swigs his beer, sings along to the tunes, and looks out of the window.

Lou mind drifts to the pending dinner party, the stupid questions they will encounter; will they walk, will they talk... usual bullshit questions – not really wanting the *how are you really feeling* questions and actually listening, really listening!

No real empathy. Lou knows they will want to change the subject as soon as they can which will suit Ben. If anybody was meeting Ben for the first time, they wouldn't know he was the father of disabled twins or maybe not the fact he was even married.

Lou's anxiety builds up as they approach the house – Tristian and Esme were incredibly successful. Esme part-owned a beauty business but she didn't really work. Other people did the work. She just took a salary, adding to her allowance from Tristian. Esme was basically a socialite. Tristian had had various businesses and made his initial money selling off his parents' farm, acre by acre, building by building. Avoiding tax and using the cash to build a UK version of renovation hardware and he was also a CEO of a very well-funded data science start up, absolutely loaded. Although lovely and well-connected, they were pretty superficial people. Lou both enjoyed and endured their company before Ted and Holly were born and never thought she would be so anxious going to their new house. Life had changed so significantly for Lou and all the talk, and the show just left her cold. Lou had more time now for people like Di and Jez – real people with real lives. Giving up their life, time, and effort for others. Lou often just couldn't understand where her head was, why so conflicted within 12 months? Where was the old Lou? Was she dead and buried for good?

They pull up to the modern-style home, geometric shapes, lots of large glass windows and sharp angles optimising the ostentatious new build. Down and up lighters everywhere, lighting up the outside like Blackpool illuminations. Stone, grey metal architecture and cedar panels surrounded this Silicon Valley style masterpiece. Living walls covered in plants were on the outside and large, tall, sculpted privet and conifers lead from the drive to the large double doors. This had been built by Ferg's building business and was one of his local showpiece homes.

Ferg was a builder, rough and ready. But he'd gone from a plasterer to owning a thriving small development business focusing on wealthy clients generating great profit margins, tidy personal wealth, and a beautiful new property. A great living life statement for all his hard graft over the years. A larger-than-life character, Ferg had bridged the social divide from subcontracting brick layer to mixing it with the local millionaires and the elite clique.

Ferg had met Ben years ago down the local and they enjoyed each other's company. They were normal lads into golf, football, and boozing. A beer and a line now and then kept the party going. Ferg and Rach had become good friends with Ben and Lou pre twins, and they enjoyed a lot of good times together especially skiing and Salcombe by the beach. Money wasn't an issue for Ferg and Rach and they could keep up with the cash side, but Courcheval 1850 and Salcombe attracted a certain type of clientele that Ferg wasn't always comfortable with, especially when they looked down at him. Ferg always fired back quickly, his humour and quick wit helped he kept up verbally and financially. He would tend to steer away from his education which was a weak spot, so he masterfully crafted conversations away to sport or current affairs. He may not have been academically top, but there was no denying that he'd built a beautiful house for Tristian and Esme.

Lou's heart sinks as they pull through the large prison-style grey 10-foot gates. Making their way through the oversized planters, they park at the oak framed garage.

Lou takes a few shallow and them some deep breaths. Ben looks up from his phone as they pull into the drive – 'One day Lou, eh?'

Ben and Lou are first to arrive. *This is all I need, nowhere to hide*, Lou thinks.

They get out of the car and press the bell, but there's no need the high security CCTV system has already picked them up. Ben holds back, looking at the finely manicured garden, grey slate, and huge Zen water feature.

Esme opens the door. 'Hi, so great to see you.'

'Hi, lovely to see you Esme, how are you?' Lou says, handing over the obligatory flowers, chocolates, and champagne.

'Thank you – so lovely, very kind of you both!'

Double kisses all round – 'Hi, Tristian, lovely to see you.' MWAH - MWAH

'So good to see you so sorry to hear about you know...the twins.'

'So sorry' really!' Lou thinks.

'Yes, well they're alive Tristian, that's the main thing, eh!' Lou says, moving past Ben and making her way around the room.

Lou knew this would happen and this was exactly the start she was hoping to avoid. Tristian stutters and doesn't know where to put himself.

'Yes, alive yes,' he says. 'Can I show you the new pool?'

Lou lets him off the hook. 'Sure, let's see the new pool.'

Esme chimes in – 'Oh no, wait Tristian. The others are arriving shortly, let's hold the tour until were all together.'

'Oh, sorry Es didn't realise – sorry guys hold we will do the grand tour the others arriving now.'

Oh yes press hold, Grand Tour FFS, Lou thinks.

Esme's life had always been one of privilege. Wealthy parents had pushed her through the local private school. She had got her place through a series of connections and back doored her way in. Her first husband had been a professional rugby player who had met her when she was at school and, although she was under 16 and he was over 18, he used to pick her up from the school gate. Esme loved the attention of being picked up by the local sporting hero in his sports car. Esme's dad was a classic car collector. Her summer weekends were garden parties and classic car shows hanging out of her father's Bentley or Rolls Royce. Esme loved the attention and as she moved into her late teens was known as the 'party girl' around town – West Bridgford's very own 'It girl'. If there was a society party Esme would be there. She also loved to slum it and had fallen into the group late through the children's school – the children all got on well.

By the time twins came along Esme was on her third marriage, two pays offs had kept her in the lifestyle she had become accustomed to. Special needs twins were not on Esme's agenda and since the full extent of the twin's brain damage became apparent, she had distanced herself from Lou. The odd smile and 'hello darling' were about it. When the twins were born, Esme was one of the ones that did share her 'condolences and was so sorry to hear what had happened'. Shortly after they were born Esme had caught Lou at a tired, low moment who snapped back at her 'the twins were alive, you know.' Waiting for the rest of the group to arrive, Lou could feel the tension between her and Esme. Ben was totally oblivious, chatting away to Tristian about the cost of the house.

Toby, Lexi, Phil, Hetty, Fran, Aidan, Rachel and Ferg all arrive as posse in an 8-seater. *Thanks for the invite*, Lou thinks, but realises they are out of the loop, and it must be too much like hard work to organise around their issues.

Lou stands back and Ben goes to the door with Esme and Tristian. *Weird*, Lou thinks.

The party has defiantly started now the 'Team' are here.

There are MWAH MWAH's all-round as they all sidle in with the wine, chocolates, gifts, flowers, and Aidan's even brought some cheese (his favourite). They have obviously stopped at a few pubs on the way and their arrival raises the volume in the room by a few notches. Tristian turns his playlist on through his phone and 14 Bang and Olufsen speaker sound system, obviously.

The group settles into 'mingling mode' and now Lou has her ground cover, hiding amid the small talk. She's lost her mojo and is struggling. Where has the confident 'old Lou' gone? She's still not shaken off the baby weight and is self-conscious, feeling a little plump. Her old fitness regime has gone out of the window, and she knows she shouldn't feel like this, but she can't help it. As Lou surveys the room, she is envious of the 'beach body' ready women, particularly Hetty. Lou doesn't understand why she cannot deal with it, these are her oldest friends. Their kids are best friends and they have always been best of friends.

What's changed in and about me? Lou wonders. Apart from checking her phone every three minutes in case she is needed by Di and Jez. But there is just radio silence, it's a good thing but not a good thing for the new Lou as the regimented, relentless care has consumed her. All of her. Lou really struggles to feel like her old self and relax, just enjoying the company of friends who are very much enjoying each other's company.

Tristian taps his ornate wine glass, calling the room to the royal visit of the pool and gym. Lou thinks, *yawn!* The group Whoops then they're off like a load of children on a zoo visit. Woahs, wows and gasps of breath erupt from the fawning crowd as they are shown round the Hilton-hotel-style pool covered in brown fake marble panelling and terrazzo flooring. There are even tacky Roman bloody statues and pillars in every colour. The end of the room features two teak loungers with Versace towels that have been embroidered with Tristian and Esme's initials. *Yuck,* Lou thinks, but she joins in, cupping her mocktail – 'Wow looks amazing, you have done such a good job.'

Tristian stands back, hips thrust forward with that 'look at me, look at me' proud stance. Esme stands there flicking her hair as if to say 'really, we hadn't noticed how nice it was!' Lou saunters off into the background, bored.

The procession then makes their way to the gym which doubles as viewing area for the pool. Lou feels it's like being back on the viewing balcony and café area at school, like when her parents watched her swim. Quite hilarious! It must have cost a fortune and, joking aside, was quite impressive. On the tour, Ben is in his element, talking to Hetty and Rach, laughing and flirty, holding court (as usual) and knocking back the beers at a rate, topping himself up.

The Gym and seating area is pretty ostentatious (and cold) like a hotel foyer – dark browns, copper, and gold everywhere.

They walk the group round as if they are being toured around the bloody Sagrada Familia.

The gaggle eventually make their way back to the kitchen/ dining area, the music is cranked up and the chit chat starts.

Lou is in a large group with all the women and just listens in.

Then Lexi turns to her. 'How are you, love?'

'Well, you know. A lot to work through!'

Lexi is desperate not to get into too much detail and is just look at Lou uncomfortably. 'Oh ok, how's Ben's work doing?'

'Ben's very busy, you know, on the promotion front.'

Lou then knows the drill, 'How are you, Lexi?'

This is a tactic that Lou was used to using regularly in person or digitally; reframe and put the focus back on the other person's life as they love talking about themselves.

Finally, the lighting is dimmed, and everyone is asked to sit at the table. The place settings are set out for the group, they find their spot and are seated, and drinks are poured by someone in a black outfit who Lou doesn't recognise. It was strange that they were having dinner and there was no frantic cooking, smoke, and empty baking trays all over. Apart from the Perollo olives, artisan bread, olive oil and balsamic vinegar, the worktops were clear and no ovens on. Even the eight-ringed, mirrored ceramic hob had flowers on it.

What Lou had failed to realise was there was another kitchen tucked away like a servants' quarter. In addition to the separate kitchen, where the cooking smells wouldn't go to war with the Jo Malone room infusers, a small army of cooks and helpers were busy creating the food extravagance, serving it, and cleaning up and taking all the crockery away. This was a full-on catering event. As they sit the food is served and the chef comes out and introduces himself as Alfonso, a protégé of Sat Bains, basically a wannabe celebrity chef who had appeared on ITV Be or something. Lou had switched off. She was too busy laughing inside at Esme who just sat, her lips pursed, nodding listening intently to the chef's every word. Esme looks round the table to ensure everyone is suitable impressed and as she looks at Lou, Lou raises her alcohol-less Mojito.

Alfonso completes his run down of the starter and paired wine and the group give him a round of applause.

Lou is nestled between Aidan and Phil, her worst nightmare as these two are the hardest people to speak to. Aidan lacks any empathy, was clumsy, driven, and materialistic. Phil, Hetty's husband, was just so dull and hated dinner parties more than Lou. Lou's new world was a million miles away from this world. She knew that they had no comprehension of the last year, the effect on her family and about the twins condition. The last thing either of them wanted or needed to hear about was her family's daily struggles.

The conversation started with the usual formalities. Then Aidan jumps in first, 'How are Jake and Megan?'

'Great, thank you.' Lou says before talking about the normal side of the family, what her older kids are up to with school and sport. She asks politely about their children and what they are up to and has remember their son Rory was excelling at his sport. 'How's Rory doing with his rugby and cricket?'

'Yes, doing great. He has been picked up by the East Midland squad and the county cricket selectors. England rugby and cricket better watch out.'

Great, well done fucking Rory, Lou thinks, but instead says, 'Oh, that's great news.'

The conversation goes on for 10 minutes or so and main course arrive with Alfredo talking about the home-grown carrots, rack of French trimmed lamb, and celeriac mash grown on a local community garden and various other jus and pairing wines which Lou cannot enjoy because she is driving, along with Phil who has been deathly quiet so far.

Thank God a break from Aidan's relentless bloody showing off, Lou thinks. The room goes quiet as everyone tucks in.

Aidan then builds up the energy to remember Lou has more children.

'How are the twins doing?' he asks.

Fuck me what a question, where does Lou start with this

one.

'Do you mean Ted and Holly?'

Aidan splutters on his Lamb, 'Yes, sorry Ted and Holly, how are they now?'

Now!! Like they are going to get better. When that question is asked it is a question that needs answering very succinctly.

'Yes, they are back at home, as you know. Really hard work at the moment as we have to do so much on our own with little support, It's 24 hours a day 7 days a week.' Lou takes a mouthful of food and the silence in the room is deafening. Ferg chimes in with a sneery smile. 'Yes, all kids are hard work aren't they gang!'

As the group titter, Hetty steps in before Lou explodes. 'No Ferg, not just kid hard work, real hard work. A lot of needs over and above.'

Ben looks longingly at Hetty.

Lou knows that he has always had a thing for Hetty, younger than Lou and she always joked that Hetty must have got all the good genes.

Ferg takes a sip of wine and nods, clearly wanting the ground to swallow him up.

Lexi jumps in and asks Lou, 'How have you been Hun...?'

Hun! just fuck off with that one 'M.I.A Lexi'. Where and how have you been over the last year Hun, yourself!!

'Well, you know, OK. Thanks Lexi. What about you, been away yet?'

Lou's usual tactics work a treat and Lexi freestyles about her last and next city break. Lou disappears into the conversation of others listening, smiling, and nodding in the right place.

Lou keeps all of the conversations to her 'normal' children, the generic stresses, and strains of bringing up kids, school, teachers etc. She knows that this group do not want to hear the reality of bringing up a disabled family. Lexi goes on to talk about the wish for a Blue Parking badge so she could park on double yellows on West Bridgford high street when she picks up her soy latte from 200 degrees. Lou is exasperated. As she looks out the window thinking of the twins and how they are doing, she sees the security lights come on and two hooded figures on push bikes pull into the drive, one with what looks like a granny's bike with a shopping basket on the front and the other on a mountain bike. The doorbell rings and certain members of the party start smirking to each other. Ferg mutters under his breath 'Raleigh boys are here!'

Lou knows this means the drugs have arrived. Ferg rushes to the door and comes back grinning and with a stupid smirk, shouts to the room 'desert's here!' The room erupts into laughter and cheers. Lou dips in and out of the conversations when she feels it appropriate but, on the whole, keeps pretty quiet, drinks her mocktails, smiles and listens. Ben is smashing the drinks back now and laughing with his arms stretched out around Hetty and Fran's shoulders – who are loving it. Ben hasn't spoken about or acknowledged Ted and Holly in any way.

So, as the main courses come to an end, half the table including Ben get up for a cigarette – Lou hates this bit as it can get really focused on her.

She is left with Ferg, Rachel, Aidan, and Phil.

Ferg, a builder by trade but now more of a developer, has done incredibly well and has always had a great relationship with Lou, they used to have such a laugh together. Ferg asks genuinely how Lou is actually doing.

Lou gives a sort of half answer, 'You know, sort of ok. Sleep's not great and we are just starting to meet social workers and other health care professionals. It's full on, you know, Ferg.'

Ferg gives a sympathetic nod and looks down.

Rach, Ferg's trophy wife, isn't Lou's bag at all. All Monclur, first class this and D&G that, it has never impressed Lou in anyway, now even less so.

Then Rach pipes up. 'Oh well you know Hun; you've just got to get on with it haven't you?'

Lou looks at Rach in absolute incredulity, *where do I*

fucking start with that one...Averting WW3 and killing off the night off completely. Lou just replies, 'Oh yes Rach, you have to just get on with it and we are getting through it, we are working through it but all new learnings, you know, Hun!'

Lou looks up. Thank God the 'smoking gang' arrive back from their break before dinner is served by the caterers/chefs/ waiters... whoever they are!

Now on a different level, Lou is feeling completely sober. The excessive garlic has dried her out and she gets on the water.

The evening is flowing nicely around the table, and she avoids any talk of the twins.

Esme is talking about birthing pools, and she avoids all talk of births.

Aidan and Fran who have twins themselves dive into the conversation and start to talk about the amazing care they received when Fran gave birth. How incredible the hospital was all set up and organised for the birth with 'an army' of professionals and how truly amazing it all was.

God, really!

Lou nods politely, avoiding everyone's gaze, thinking please don't not ask me anything. Giving birth is amazing and should be amazing but it wasn't for us so save this joyous conversation for another time preferably when we are not here – THANK YOU!

Conversation switches to birth stories and Lou finds herself wandering off to the loo which is a little way away. Great timing. She takes her time, hoping the 'wonderful' birth stories have ended by the time she returns. Wandering back, she admires the home that Tristian had built. It wasn't really her taste, but it was impressive none the less.

Back at the table, the subject has moved on from births and onto sport – Lou thinks, *great I can listen and nod.*

Ben has hardly spoken to Lou and is now in deep conversation with Hetty – God knows what about. He is now rat-arsed and obviously not going to be doing much tomorrow with the kids. It will take all of Lou's efforts to get him away from the party as they need to be back at 12am latest.

She's flagging badly; this time of night is her first period of sleep before the twins get restless and need attending to. 9pm is late to sleep for Lou so 11pm is positively the middle of the night.

Lou cannot believe how knackered and bored she is and tries to get Ben's attention, giving him the 'I am ready' eyes. He fires back his 'just one more look' eyes.

Esme puts on the Ibiza classics, turns the music up and disco lights under the worktop and around the kitchen appear from nowhere.

Lou knows where this is going and needs to get Ben out before she loses him.

'Ben, are you ready?' she asks.

'Can't we stay? It's just getting going. Can't we stay and just pay the carers for another hour?'

'Ben, we need to relieve Di and Jez.' Lou sighs.

'I know, but it's just getting going –'

'Ben!'

'Hetty said they can drop me back on their way back,' Ben pleads.

'Fucks sake Ben. Really. You know how hard things are at home. There's no point me arguing, you're staying, aren't you?'

'I'll be back later,' he says, putting a full stop on the conversation.

This had happened before, and Lou knew what it meant – it's ok to escape for a night, but Lou knows what this means for her.

'Don't be late.'

Lou slides away unnoticed by the rest of the gang and jumps in the car and drives like its stolen to get back for the 12am deadline. Lou hates being late, especially for the kind people helping with the twins.

As Lou turns the key in the door and creeps back into the house, Di and Jez are right there with reassuring smiles and assurances for Lou. Both are watching the twins diligently on the monitors. All is well and the twins are fast asleep. Lou breathes a huge sigh of relief. She is back ready to pick up the care.

'Hi both, how have they been?' she asks.

'A little unsettled. Ted has been awake a lot. We did as you said and gently rocked the cots,' Di reports.

'He took his milk, ok?'

'Yes, he took most of it, but just really unsettled can be hard to tell sometimes.'

'Is he ok now?'

'Yes, all good. How's it been expressing?' Di enquires.

'Expressing milk for two has been tricky and I was constantly leaking but managing to capture enough, just.'

'It's a good thing Lou, keep going, you're doing great.'

'Was Megan, ok?' Lou asks.

'Yes, she stirred but I rocked her cot, and she went back off.'

'Thanks to you both,' Lou says.

While she is glad to be back in control of the twins, she feels a pang of dread as her safety net disappears out the door. These nights provided by healthcare volunteers through health are rare will end as the twins get to the age of four. Respite care like this through social care is non-existent.

Lou waves them off and starts to close down the house, leaving the hall and outside light on for Ben and turns on the CCTV next to the bed to watch over the children all night. She tries to drift off with one eye always open and a mother's listening instinct to wake when the children need her.

As Lou dips into sleep, she thinks about the stark comparison between her friends and family and the trained, competent kind carers that had given their time up for the children.

Lou sparks awake and checks the twins once more on the CCTV – they are fine. She drifts off into an extremely light sleep.

She remembers checking the clock in between the twins

waking; 1.30am, 2.15am, 3.15am. The twins wake on and off all night, as if pre-coordinated not to wake at the same time. Still no Ben. From 3.15am both children go into a deep sleep, Lou checks her phone to check for texts from Ben.

Lou texts Ben 'where are you.' Nothing back.

Lou wrestles with her anger and struggles to get to sleep herself. She takes a couple of paracetamols as she has a blistering headache – not from the alcohol but from the change in sleep pattern as she is much later to bed than usual.

With almost no sleep, her body clock wakes her at 6am as usual. This is usually 15-20 minutes before the twins wake and it gives Lou time to compose herself. As she wakes, she looks across the bed. Ben had made his way home at some point. Lou was oblivious but knew this meant Ben would be hung over for the whole day, offer nothing and want to just chillax all day.

Jake and Megan are due back at 9am from mum's so Lou needs to get ready for this and start her morning routine alone.

The twins are still small enough to be lifted, changed, and fed which helps Lou as she picks up the care again. Chuntering to herself about her 'selfish, useless twat of a husband' who will no doubt wake looking for sympathy, she finishes the children's morning routine. Taking a breather, she turns on the kettle. Then at the door the walking dead appears looking like absolute shit.

'Can I have one?' Ben asks.

'Yes, let me do that as well. The kids are fine by the way, don't worry Ben! What time did you get back?' Lou snaps.

'I don't know.'

'Why were you so late?'

Ben looks out the window, eyes half closed, hair all over the place, boxer shorts half twisted round his waist and a scraggy old t shirt with toothpastes stains on the front.

'Lou don't give me a hard time; I don't feel well.'

'Why did you stay out then?'

'We were talking and dancing in the kitchen.'

'And drinking, Ben. You were already pissed when you arrived. How did you get home.'

'Phil and Hetty I think. Phil wasn't drinking.'

'God, that was lucky. Make sure you text and thank them today.'

'Sure.' Ben continues to walk round in circles, half burping, half retching.

'Here, have this.' Lou says, passing him the coffee she just made him.

'Cheers, I am going out for a tuvla,' he says, taking out his cigarette packet.

'Maybe say hi to your children, Ben,' Lou says.

'Oh yes, sorry!'

Ben leans over and kisses the twins on their foreheads and walks to the back door.

As Ben walks back in letting Lou know that he is going for a shower, Jake and Megan arrive back.

'Hi Jake, hi Megan, do you want some breakfast?' Lou asks.

'No thanks, we have already had it. Thanks mum.' Megan replies.

As the family are all now back together for the weekend, Lou feels she has five children to look after. As Ben makes his way down in his loungewear, Lou knows that her day will be another day at home after spending all week at home.

'What are you doing today, Ben?'

Ben's blank expression says everything.

'Er, I will get Jake to football for 11am and then home, is that ok?'

Great you get out and I am stuck here all day, again, Lou thinks.

Ben sprawls out on the sofa shouting instructions to Jake to get his football gear ready and asks Lou for another coffee and bacon sandwich.

Lou just sucks it and up gets him a coffee. As she delivers it to the sofa she leans down sternly, with a smile tells Ben to 'get your own fucking breakfast'.

As Ben disappears out of the door, Lou gets the twins ready for the outdoors and gets Megan ready for a walk into West Bridgford for some fresh air, a coffee, cake, and time with her girl.

Another groundhog weekend begins.

Chapter 9
Culpability

Christmases, birthdays, and anniversaries came and went. The family circle of friends and relatives was reducing and reducing as the impacts of their situation took hold of every element of their life. Four years after their exchange with Vik's and starting their medical negligence claim. Vikesh called Lou and Ben out of the blue and asks that they meet, but not to the local office. To the barristers in Birmingham at 9am the following week. Vikesh wouldn't say anymore, just that he had a response from the hospital which needed discussing.

Lou and Ben make the necessary arrangements for the twins to be looked after. They cannot risk driving down on the morning with traffic, so decide to travel down the night before. The twins are cared for in a relay with Hetty taking the night shift and a raft of carers covering the rest. Hetty knows how important the meeting is, agrees to her first and only care shift after Lou pleads with her sister. They need to be 100% focused as this is potentially life changing for the family.

As the parents get ready to leave, chucking overnight stuff in a bag, they speak to the carers that have arrived for the twins, going through the handover sheets and care plan as quickly as they can. The twins are safely in bed but awake. The parents are still giving instructions as they head out the door to start their journey. They both dump themselves into the car and breathe a massive sigh of relief, turn on their old 90's station and leave West Bridgford to the sounds of The Happy Mondays.

The car journey is incredibly peaceful, and both Ben and Lou sit in silencer listening to Absolute 90's and reminisce as each song comes on, remembering where they were when they heard it or the venue where they saw the band. Those days are long gone but it's a strange feeling of freedom, if only for one night.

Ben had booked the Malmaison on his credit card and the Ivy for dinner. Hugely expensive but Ben's reasoning was 'we are close by to the office to minimise the risk of being late' Lou was kept away from the finances.

They walk up the impressive steps of the Mailbox to Malmaison's entrance and head straight to reception to check in. Lou has a lovely warm feeling as this harks back to their early days as a couple exploring the cities of UK and Europe. It felt edgy, cheeky and a little dangerous, – a night of respite to forget the twins and their regime at home.

Opening the door to the pristine hotel room without the stains and clutter of everyday life, Lou felt a tingle of longing and suggested a little time together in the room. But Ben turned cold, saying they should go straight for drinks before dinner, edging away from Lou to change into his jeans and a fresh shirt. Ben empties his bag out, hangs his suit bag and encourages Lou to do the same so they could go straight to the bar. Lou is disappointed as closeness is not something they get time for, and she misses the connection they had. Ben was cold these days, and even when they get the chance turns her away. As they leave the room, Ben kisses Lou and with a robotic 'I love you' they leave for the warmth of the bar and alcohol.

The bar is buzzing, full of couples and businesses people

enjoying a drink after work or settling in for the night. Ben orders a Stella and a Pinot Grigio for Lou. He smashes back the pint in just a few gulps. They talk about the meeting and the twins and little else. Ben is confident that they have a case, and that the news tomorrow will be that the hospital has caved under legal scrutiny. They talk about what they are going to do when they get the compensation and their day in court to face the wrongdoers. Ben wants this all over the press – Lou is not so sure. The couple are feeling positive they will win the case. They both feel deep down that the hospital cover up will be uncovered – it's a done deal. Ben smashes back another five beers whilst Lou gently sips her first glass. But then she's encouraged to buy a bottle by Ben.

As they leave the Malmaison for the Ivy, they walk the busy streets of Birmingham talking lucidly. They hold hands and it feels great. Both are 'merry' as they walk through the door of the Ivy. Shown to the table, Ben asks for the wine list from the sommelier.

He goes straight for the 'heavy reds' and orders a bottle of his go to, Châteauneuf-du-Pape all for himself and bottle of Sancerre for Lou. As it's delivered to the table, Lou asks for a bottle of sparkling water. This is way more than Lou would normally drink and the booze is kicking in, so water is essential.

Ben is now 'on one' and orders caviar for starter and lobster for main. Lou wades in with gravlax and monkfish. She is being carried along on the tide of extravagant living, reassured by Ben's confidence in their financial situation.

Now in great spirits, Ben and Lou relive stories of old and the music back in the day. Those landmark gigs: The mighty Lemon Drops, Carter USM, Nirvana, Blur and Pulp at Rock City, Latitude and holidays with friends, the roller discos, and the night they met, acting like two young lovers on a date. The wine is flowing, and they forget quietly why they are in Birmingham. The meal finishes with two brandies and deconstructed Ferrero Rocher. Ben puts the bill on the latest credit card to arrive, and they are off.

The rest of the night is lost in a cloud of stumbling and giggling to the city's CCTV and behind the bedroom door of the Malmaison room 187.

The alarm sounds and Lou wakes, bleary eyed and incredibly hung over.

Ben raises his head from the pillow. 'What time is it?'

'7am.'

'Shit,' he mumbles. 'What time did we get in?'

'Don't know,'

Ben gets up and goes to the toilet, joking from the bathroom that 'it smells of sugar puffs,' still slightly pissed and giggling to himself.

The rooms like a bomb site, stinks of stale booze like a tap room floor with clothes everywhere. Ben brushes his teeth through the retching – hunched over the sink.

Lou props herself up, hair everywhere with smudged make-up still intact.

'Ben, I feel like shit. How long have we got?'

'Good night though, babe.' Ben grins. 'About an hour and a bit.'

'Right, I will shower.'

God, I need to eat.'

'We can get something on the way. Let's check out, get near where we need to be, so we are not late and find a café.'

As they wander down the hotel steps and through the streets of Birmingham hardly a word is spoken, dressed in suits with overnight bags and a filing box with correspondence just in case there is a vital bit of evidence to get this over the line.

They find the offices and decide to wander around looking for a nice café.

'We've only got 30 minutes. I feel like shit. I need to eat,' Ben whines.

'Greggs!' Lou says, pointing at the blue and yellow signage.

'I am not going to Greggs, Lou.'

'Well, that's all there is.'

'Jesus.'

They sit down for breakfast at a rickety aluminium chair and table covered in crumbs, somebody else's unfinished breakfast and empty cups. Workers saunter in and out, grabbing a quick breakfast or coffee on the go.

They look across the table at each other, red eyed, pale, and gingerly munch their way through greasy sausage rolls and bitter coffee.

'I cannot finish this, Ben, it's rank,' Lou says.

'Eat what you can. I'm not sure how long we are going to be in this meeting, and we need to go straight back home after.'

'I think I am going to be sick if I eat any more,' Lou says.

The half-eaten breakfast and half-drunk coffee cups are left, and they grab their luggage and box files.

Feeling a shade better than they did, they walk down the street to the offices. Behind the anonymous doorway lies the answer to the question they have been hanging onto all these years, and a brand-new future.

The lift is out of order so Ben and Lou humph their luggage and files up the stairs, and they make their way up the comprehensive-school-like beige, coffee-stained, lino stairs to the reception on floor 6.

They take a breath at the top and are sweating out the grapes profusely. Lou wafts a file in front of her face, composing herself.

Ben slinks up to the reception desk and holds court with the two young receptions who Lou can see giggling and flicking their hair around. Still slightly pissed, Ben is feeling frisky. Lou feels like death and doesn't have time for Ben's antics. She goes through the box file to make sure they have everything, swallowing deeply and walks over to the water fountain and swigs back cup after cup.

A few unknown faces walk through reception and eventually Vik's comes out though the mahogany door at the bottom.

He shakes Ben's hand and kisses Lou on the cheek, leading

them to a large conference room. A vast boardroom table dominates the space, surrounded by leather desk chairs.

At the table at the end of the room, there are a couple of unknown faces who are poised to take notes alongside Sanjeet the barrister who they have met briefly. Sanjeet is a tall, immaculately dressed man, well-spoken and incredibly sharp. He gets up and welcomes the couple in and they are asked if they want a tea or coffee by one of the note takers. Heads thumping, both choose coffee and, as it's delivered, smash down the custard creams to help absorb the hangover.

In front of Sanjeet is a thick brown envelope, what appears to be hospital notes and annotated documents. Ben and Lou unload their files, A4 pad, various pens, and highlighters ready for action. Having finished off the custard creams, they both take a big slug of coffee and compose themselves. The room is silent.

Sanjeet leads as Vikesh sits back with a blank expression on his face. Their solicitor is fidgety and keeps rubbing his chin, covering his mouth, and looking at Sanjeet to avoid Ben and Lou's gaze.

Lou is desperately trying not to throw up and reaches for a glass of water.

'Thank you both for coming today. I have now heard back from Talbert's acting for the defendant's, the trust, and a follow up from legal aid,' Sanjeet says.

Ben and Lou sit forward, knowing this is the moment that could change everything.

'It's not great news I am sorry to say,' Sanjeet continues.

'What? Why? What's been said?' Ben is aghast.

Lou's head drops.

'I have had the notes back from the night.'

'Can we see them?'

'Yes. These are the midwives, SHO's and the registrar,' Sanjeet says, passing across the pieces of paper.

Ben scours through the notes to get to the timings as soon as he can...

'10 minutes! 10 minutes – they are still saying 10 minutes. This cannot be right. Where's the SHO's notes?' Ben exclaims.

As Ben gets through to the SHO's recollections in the notes he looks up at Sanjeet in complete amazement.

'These are the same. What's going on here?!'

'I understand this isn't the news you were looking for but it's what we have had back and does make things extremely challenging.'

'And the registrar?' Ben asks.

'The same, 10 minutes.'

'This is a fucking joke.' Ben pushes back into his chair and puts his hands behind his head. Lou's eyes are filled with tears as she scans the paper in front of her.

'I cannot believe this,' she says. 'There's no way it was 10 minutes. It wasn't 10 minutes!'

Vikesh doesn't know where to look. He sits forward with his hands clasped in front of him on the desk.

'I am sorry this isn't the news you wanted.'

'4 years to get to this! Nothing! They will not accept that the delays THEY caused through staff incompetence – NOTHING?!' Ben is filled with rage.

'What did their solicitors say?' Lou asks.

'They back up the trust and say there is no case to answer, regrettable but just one of those things, within the window and a natural risk of childbirth,' Sanjeet says.

'What about the birth plan and Epidural – we were high risk!' Lou says.

'They say all risks were assessed and everything was in place as much as it could be. 10 minutes was just not enough time to deliver the anaesthetic and get the twins out. The Trust did all they could in the 10-minute window in which they delivered the twins. 10-minutes and just beyond is the window of acceptability.'

'The notes are bullshit – it wasn't 10 minutes!' Ben says, slamming his fist on the desk.

'What about the machine in the room that recorded the

twins - that will surely show, clearly the timing wont it?' Lou tries.

'The CTG? The CTG has gone missing and cannot be found. We only have the notes,' Sanjeet says.

'That's just wrong.'

'10 minutes is the line they are sticking to, and they are saying that it was well inside the acceptable for delivering twin's. The notes all align.'

'This is just bullshit, what can we do?'

Well, that's the problem, Ben, the third component is the access to legal aid. They have assessed the case and have given it zero chance of success and wish to close the case. To move forward you will need to fund the next stages if you wish to proceed,' Sanjeet says.

Vik's then steps in, 'Ben, I know you are counting on this, and things aren't easy at the moment, is there a chance you could fund the next steps? Do you want to press on?'

'What do you mean counting on this, Ben? For the twins, right?' Lou says.

Vik's takes a hard look at Ben.

'We will talk about this later, Lou,' Ben murmurs.

Lou opens her mouth again but Vik's steps in. 'To get your costs back and to fund the future costs over and above for bringing up disabled twins.'

'What costs are we going to get back?' Lou asks.

'It's complicated, let's talk about it later,' Ben says.

Sanjeet looks awkwardly at Vik's.

Vik's knows that Ben has been keeping a file of costs to put on the Trust that were not entirely legitimate and that he had been creating invoices for equipment and care. Ben had been counting on this as a guaranteed win, and this was his way out of all of the financial issues he had created and get his debtors off his back. In Ben's mind it was a done deal.

'Ben, can we pursue this? We still have money in the house and could get a loan. We have to pursue this. They are wrong and we know this is not the truth. Can we do this?' Lou asks.

Ben knows that there is no money on the house, they already have loans that are in both names where he has forged Lou's signature. Credit cards in both names with forged signatures with Lou's card hidden safely away in a shoe box. They can hardly afford the repayment interest, never mind a 6-figure court battle.

'If you wish to pursue, we need to know now as we have 14 days to reply, or the case will be closed down for good. Our legal window will close on Friday. We have the contract to work with us here ready to sign,' Sanjeet says.

'Ben, we need to carry on. We have to get to the truth,' Lou pleads.

Ben sheepishly looks down and is sweating profusely, shuffling on his chair.

'I am sorry guys we cannot agree to this at this stage,' he says.

Ben knows this is the end of the line, is embarrassed and cannot look Lou in the eye.

'I can talk to mum and dad, what about your mum and dad?' Lou asks Ben.

But Ben has already been onto both parents for significant cash and has kept from Lou to protect her.

'Lou, we cannot go forward at this point and need to talk about this later.'

Lou is distraught and cannot understand Ben's lack of fight.

Sanjeet apologises to them both and shuffles up his paperwork.

'We will consider this mater closed and wish you all the very best. If you manage to put the funding in place let us know and we will help where we can. Should any more evidence come to light please let Vik's know. We will close out with legal aid. You may get some correspondence from us confirming what we have agreed today.'

The note takers then close their pads and put down their pens.

The room is deafening quiet. Vik's gets up to lead Ben and Lou out. Sanjeet gets up and moves to the door.

'Good luck to you both in the future,' he says.

Ben waits for Vik's to follow them out and as soon as Lou goes to the toilet, he pulls Vik's to one side.

'Why the fuck didn't you say something Vik's!!'

'I couldn't, mate. I needed you to hear this from Sanjeet, I didn't know myself until this morning that we had to drop the case. I needed to understand the implications of legal aid being dropped, and what we would be the next steps.'

'You know I am fucked financially, Vik's.'

'I understand, mate.'

'Can we go to another barrister?'

'You know pal, this will be tricky without serious funding,' Vik's says.

'How much?'

'£100k plus but could be more end to end and take another 5-6 years.'

'5-6 years ??!! That's a lifetime Vik's. What are the chances of success?'

'We need more evidence of delays but would need to clearly show a level of negligence.'

'What sort of evidence?'

'Written or a witness.'

'A nurse?'

'Yes, a nurse, doctor or similar.'

'You know how hard that would be don't you?'

'Yes, I understand but we would need that evidence and the financial backing.'

Lou opens the door.

'Vik's, I need this. We need this,' Ben says through gritted teeth.

'I understand Ben, stay in touch.'

Ben knew this was the end of the road for a legal challenge. Vik's had exposed their position way to early, allowing the hospital and the legal team to get their ducks in a row. Vik's lack of knowledge in this area had blown any chance of a case against the hospital to expose the lie, giving time for notes to be aligned and for the CTG evidence to be conveniently misplaced. Ben knew what this meant for their future. They were alone and this struggle would have to be battled without the financial cushion a negligence claim would have given them. Already 'up to his back axles in debt', there was no escape cord for Ben to pull and this sent him spiralling.

As they dragged their overnight bags, files, and folders out of the offices they walk back to in silence, slowly through the streets of Birmingham.

They get in the car and as they both sit staring forward, Lou turns to Ben. 'We need to find the money.'

'Lou, it's complicated. We just can't at the moment.'

'We have the house...'

'We do, but we cannot raise any more on the house.'

'Why not?'

'I have used some of the money to help us get by when you finished work.'

'How much, Ben?'

'£75k.' Ben mumbles.

'£75k? How much is left?'

'Not a lot, there have been a lot of expenses going out.'

'Why did you not mention this to me earlier?' Lou says, anger rising.

'There was just never the right time. Let's talk when we get home. I am shattered, Lou.'

Ben turns up the volume to break the silence as they make the 2-hour drive home through heavy traffic. A song comes on, one not heard for what seems a lifetime, but both listen intently to the meandering melody, the lyrics strike a chord with both parents as they try and comprehend what they have just been told and what the future now holds.

"Don't worry about the future or worry but know that worrying Is as effective as trying to solve an algebra equation by chewing Bubble gum.

The real troubles in your life are apt to be things that never crossed your worried mind.

The kind that blindsides you at 4 p.m. on some idle Tuesday".

This lyric really resonated with both, and they glance at each other, telepathically agreeing; this is us. Tuned into every lyric, they listen to every word Baz Luhrmann speaks through the song.

"The race is long and, in the end, it's only with yourself".

"Be nice to your siblings, they're your best link to your past and the people most likely to stick with you in the future".

"Understand that friends come and go but a precious few, who should hold on".

"Work hard to bridge the gaps in geography and lifestyle for as the older you get the more you need the people you knew when you were young".

So many themes in the song rang true to both as they travelled back, reeling from the knowledge that they were on their own and life beyond today would be precarious.

Lou never forgot the song and played it regularly when she had a free moment to herself – which was rare.

Ben stayed silent, not mentioning that on top of the big re-mortgage was tens of thousands of pounds on credit cards and loans – that was for another time or never to be discussed unless he had to. He just needed one of his big bests to come through and then it would all disappear.

The big bet on a medical negligence claim was the first to fail, leaving them in a precarious financial position.

As they pull up to the house, both take a deep breath as they take the slow walk into the house and another night of care begins.

Chapter 10

Day Out at the Reds

Ben needed to get investment and quick. A second stage payment for the housing development project in Manchester with Uncle Frank and his associates. Ben was still reeling from the news that there was no medical negligence claim to answer so any debt he had built up to file against the claim had disappeared into dust.

Nottingham Forest were playing Manchester United, and this was the perfect opportunity for Ben to put a show on for Uncle Frank and meet his elusive associates finally. Ben needed to show he was good for the money and could be trusted, it could be the answer to his big money payday and a brighter richer future.

Uncle Frank had got wind through the family that Ben may be struggling with finances so needed to suss out where Ben was. Ben needed a massive show of face to keep things on track for the big payday with the Manchester contingent. Ben has always been brilliant at 'fake it before you make it'. Great clothes, nice car, holidays, and his Rolex on his wrist, which he flashed as much as he could. On a financial knife edge for years,

Ben's lines of credit were running dry. His plethora of credit cards running on full meant his credit score was screwed.

Any incomings from his salary is now only now paying his monthly payments and interest payments on his credit cards. Lou was using any social security payments to pay for food and other household expenditure.

Ben knew that Uncle Frank loved Forest from their heyday but had moved his allegiances to fit in with his new associates who are big Red Devils fans. Ben offered up a lavish day or 'full hit' as he termed it, at the football, knowing Frank would love an away day back to Forest, his hometown club against his new love Man U. It had cost a small fortune maxing out his latest platinum credit card.

Ben's huge ego and massive over confidence would be on full display as he peacocked for the contingent from Manchester United and he just ploughed on regardless of the financial consequences.

Ben had booked brunch at the exclusive World Service restaurant in town, executive transport to the ground, a private room for beers at an exclusive club next the ground, corporate box for the day on the halfway line and a full evening of entertainment topping the day off with a chef's table at the best Indian restaurant in the centre.

Ben needed a sponsor for the day to pay for the meal, beers, transport, and expenses, so he had roped in another victim – Rob, an old school mate. Rob had been a corporate monkey all his life. He never put a foot wrong in his career and wormed his was up the slippery ladder, navigating the snake pit of individuals who operate in that world.

Ben had been warming Rob up for a while. Rob was always available as he was single and had had a good inheritance from his family.

Rob was a bit of a lost sheep. He spoke softly, had a few girlfriends but never anything really serious. His friends were all ready to accept that Rob may well be gay, and all felt it was just a matter of time before he came out. They were all cool with Rob coming out as they loved him. A great dresser, Rob would often talk about his daily and nightly skincare routine, moisturising, serums, manscaping escapades and his latest hair conditioner, much to the amusement of Friday night club in the pub. Rob would often joke about his sexuality saying he was a 'metrosexual'.

All of the boys in the pub were slightly jealous of his pristine appearance, the wives just loved Rob as he was a great conversationalist, interesting and interested, always.

Everyone had a lot of time for Rob and Ben had always stayed close to Rob. He did enjoy his company but also knew that he could work to open up an account at the bank of Rob.

Ben started to discuss the investment opportunity and wanted Rob in as a silent partner talking of 50% uplifts on his cash overtime as the development started to bear fruit. Rob was making very little interest on his cash in the bank so was all over this and had full trust in his mate.

Ben started to crank up the pressure on Rob, explaining that the Manchester contingent will be coming down with Frank and this was sign up time. When Ben spoke about the meeting with the Manchester contingent he always only explained very loosely. He would tell Rob that these were very experienced businessmen, very important people, and their word was their word. The deal would be done on a handshake and that's when it was set in stone. Ben left out the bit out drug money, gangsters, violence, prostitution, human trafficking and how this group operated and had done business. If you agree and don't pay you or you break the code of silence, you could well find yourself at the bottom of the Manchester Canal.

After making huge profits from their 'business', the gang was going legit along with Frank, filtering all of their ill-gotten gains into property and other legal ventures. The property or land was being secured through means of 'mild' extortion – brown envelopes, paying off council officials and 'mild' intimidation. They were buying huge swathes of old industrial land, derelict city centre property and old industrial areas. The gang were linked across the country and had links in Nottingham with the Hyson Green crew who were a Jamaican drug gang with their own battles with the rival Albanian gangs coming into the city. The gang had links in London, Edinburgh, Bristol, and tentacles across Europe – particularly Paris. Human trafficking had been the biggest cash earner over the last 3-4 years, and they knew they had to turn the spotlight away from this behaviour and get the cash into solid investments.

*

Laundering vast amounts of cash wasn't easy, and Frank was a prefect front to get this money moved and the right people paid discreetly. Ben had got himself involved in some of the previous beauty parades for various investments involving banks, councils, and other sellers. This was to ensure Frank's shell company got the contracts and secured the deal. Ben made himself the conduit and salesmen. The gang would be there but very much in the background, ensuring Ben towed the party line and secured the deals. Franks business partners were not ideal front men and looked, sounded, and acted like what they were; violent, intimidating and threatening. Ben knew more than he should and knew it implicated himself in the gang's dealings.

This put Ben and the family in danger, but the money, glamour and the gang's lifestyle were all too much for Ben to resist and, although clearly wrong, he pressed on, using the twins care situation and costs to justify it to himself.

Along with the property push, ironically the gang was setting up shell companies to provide services back to the government – providing contractors for commercial cleaning, dealing with secure immigration detention, asylum accommodation and support services. The gang were profiting from helping create and amplify the very issue they were providing the services to deal with for the government. Double bubble! Their immoral workings created a huge amount of cash which was tricky and long-winded to launder with massive risks. In the past, the gang and Frank had had close shaves with the Greater Manchester Police, and they knew this was a sign of what was to come, and they didn't like it. Once you were on the police's radar, you stayed on the radar. This gang was high profile since they had changed their underground dealings too legit, above ground activities, gaining press attention as they looked to transform the city.

Some of the wider gang members were already in Strangeways. If you went down, you took all the heat, kept schtum you had to just take the hit. Doing time came with the promise that their family or investment would be looked after, it kept the heat off the rest of the gang, particularly the upper echelons, while they morphed into a legit operation. The new business formula sync'd nicely with the old highly profitable enterprises. Between the old income streams and the new legit businesses, the gang were earning more money than ever. The legit businesses were flying using the same formula of extortion, intimidation and buying the right people – they were even paying tax.

The sooner they replaced business turnover from all the illegal dealings to the new model the better. There were more 'Bens' around the country who were filing 'legit' cash into the many schemes, and it needed paying on the dot or the consequences of not paying or ducking out were severe, and certainly not financial. Ben knew that he needed to keep Frank onside. Keeping Frank onside kept the organisation onside and that was the safest place to be. It would be profitable, but it would take time.

*

As the day arrives, Ben texts Frank with the itinerary. Frank replies, 'is everything in place' with a wad of dollars emoji. 'Yes, all good' Ben taps out.

Ben met up with Rob at the coffee shop prior to the

brunch meet. He got there early as everything needed to go to plan, and Rob needs to toe the party line. Ben is dressed in his very best clobber – smart casual 'race day' navy Harris tweed jacket, brown church brogues, Hugo Boss dark blue jeans, Bvlgari sunglasses and obligatory 'Roly'. As Rob arrives, Ben gives him a big hug.

'How are you doing pal let me get you a drink, what do you fancy?' Ben says.

'All good. Are you ok – Latte please?'

'Grab a table.'

Ben nervously disappears off to the counter, takes a very deep breath and orders the drink.

'Here you go, pal,' he says, putting the drink in front of Rob. 'How've you been?'

'Really good thanks. Been in Paris this week, can you remember Matilde?'

'Matilde the boss's secretary. The dancer?' Ben raises an eyebrow. 'Yes, I remember her. Did you manage to get date?'

'Yes, we had a coffee and then I took Matilde out to dinner.'

'And?'

'Well, it went really well until the end.'

'What happened at the end?'

'Turns out she's a lesbian. She really liked me, but it couldn't go any further. I slept at her place but that was as far as it went.'

'Oh shit!' Ben says, laughing.

'So that's going nowhere, you couldn't write it could you. Oh well, did it go well with the boss?' Rob asks.

'Yes, all good I am now the Chief Commercial Officer for the UK and Ireland.' Ben leans back in his seat.

'Wow, pal that's great!'

'Yes, I have to look after the buyout of the new businesses in the UK. I also get shares and performance bonuses, but it ties me in. And shares each year I stay with them.'

'That is such great news pal, I am so pleased for you,' Rob says, smiling.

As they sip their coffee there is a pause and Ben's knee jigs up and down. He needs to get it out. 'Are we all good for today?'

'Yes, all good,' Rob says.

'You happy with the £100k this week?'

'Yes, sure. Are they going to explain how this is all going to work and how we are going to realise the profit on the investment with dates?'

'Yes, they we will talk all of that over, it is as we discussed.' Ben reassures his friend. 'They are good guys and you have met Frank before.'

'Have you told them how this is going to work?'

'Yes, they know it's all through me and you are a silent partner.'

'Yes, Ben, all of this is you I am literally transferring the cash to you personally; you will then take care over everything else.'

'And you will get all you cash back and a 30% uplift, when we get our return,' Ben replies.

'Needs to be all off the books though Ben, it cannot come back on me in any way.'

'Agreed.'

'And then the next £100k will be in 8 weeks?'

'Yes, but let's get this one done first,' Ben says.

There is an awkward pause. Ben sips his coffee and then breaks the silence.

'Really looking forward to the game,' he says.

'Yes, and me.'

'What do you reckon?'

'Draw, two all.'

Ben and Rob carry on the chit chat, thoughts on the game ahead and Forest's current form, Spotify playlists and The Smiths reforming. The chat is light-hearted as Ben has the commitment he needed – it's like releasing the valve on a pressure cooker.

As they walk through the city, it's matchday and is buzzing already with fans of both persuasions walking around the market square.

They arrive at World Service first and make their way to the table. Ben nervously sits down at the huge round table facing the door, Rob sits down next to him, look like they are sat ready for an interview, awaiting the pending storm.

As they order a small breakfast beer, they keep a close eye on the door. The Manchester contingent and the group arrive with the sound of loud laughter and raised voices. The whole restaurant turns as the group arrive en mass with Frank at the front chatting to a heavy-set suited guy with a Man U scarf hanging from his neck. Most of the group walk into the dimly lit restaurant with sunglasses still on, it's like a scene from Goodfellas. Frank spots the two sat at the table and walks over. Shoulders back, dressed in a dark grey suit shimmering under the subtle lighting, he removes his sunglasses.

'Gents,' he greets them.

'Hi, Frank, how you are doing?' Ben stands up to shake his hand.

'All good.'

'Frank, you have met Rob before...' Ben says, gesturing to his friend.

'Yes, hi Rob.' Frank shakes Rob's hand.

Ben looks over Frank's shoulder and sees the rest of the travelling party coming a few steps behind. His heart races as they get closer. This is the archetypal scene out of a Scorsese film, except some are talking in broad Mancunian accents and others talking in Albanian.

Frank turns to the approaching group, 'Gentleman this is Ben who has arranged today for us.'

Ben has his hand out ready for a handshake. 'Hi all, I am Ben, and this is Rob, a very good friend of mine.'

There is a lot of nods and then one of the group steps forward. 'Hi, I am Arkan.'

Arkan is clearly a king pin in the group and takes the lead, he proceeds to introduce the group one by one. As they step forward, Ben and Rob are taken by how incredibly intimidating each one is as they remove their sunglasses and hold out their hand for a vice-like gripped handshake, nod and then return back to the rear of the group.

If Ben and Rob didn't feel nervous enough already, they were now clearly shitting themselves. This was the first time he had met the entire group and even though they were in Nottingham, on their home turf, both felt about as threatened as you they could be in the safety of a restaurant surrounded by diners.

Ever the 'glass half full', Ben was starting to realise what he had got himself into and with who. Two of the group were clearly muscle as they weren't introduced and didn't sit at the table, they sat at the bar area armed with three holdalls, which was weird for day out at the football. They sat surveying the dining area and keeping an eye on the door with their fists clenched. The feeling of menace was not lost on the other diners or the waiting staff.

Most of the table are speaking in Albanian, gesticulating aggressively with each other but smiling which Ben thought weird.

Frank turns to Ben and Rob. 'How's the family Ben?'

'OK, thanks Frank. What about you?'

'All good thanks.'

'How's Lule?'

'Lule is fine, in Marbella at the moment with girls, tanning and spending no doubt!

How are developments going with the property and the outsourcing business?'

'Growing fast.'

'That's good.'

'We have a few issues releasing money though, but I am keeping everything on track one way or the other.'

Ben knew this meant they couldn't launder fast enough to get the clean cash through, and his legit investment would be key to blend the cash. Rob just sat there nodding. Rob was like a fish out of water, sat on his hands not 100% loving what he was hearing.

'Yes, all good Frank,' Ben reassures. 'I have the date and bank details, it will all be sorted. Is everything good your side?'

'Yes, we are all good and have had planning consent for four more floors so the returns will be greater than we thought.'

'Wow, that is amazing news Frank. How did you get that through?' Ben nods, excitement rising.

'We have our ways and means Ben.' Frank taps the side of his nose and winks.

Rob is nodding like a Churchill dog.

'So, were there no objections?' Rob asks.

'We don't get objections, Rob.' Frank gins. 'We only have consenters – our friends in planning always ensure that we get the nod.'

'I see.'

'It's who you know, Rob.'

As they were talking, the loud Albanian chit chat had stopped, and the rest of the table were all intently listening to Frank, Ben, and Rob.

Arkan is staring at Frank. 'So, we're all good, Frank?'

'Yes. No issues, we are all good, everything's on track.'

A smile appears across Arkan's face. He stands up and shouts loudly to a waiter at the next table. 'Three bottles of Cristal champagne to toast a Manchester United win.'

The table all stand up and cheer, another two Man U tables join in.

The whole room looks up, it was so loud. There are a few jeers and loud mutterings from other tables with big groups of home supporters. The table remains standing and all three of the Man U tables orchestrated by Ben's table start winding up the home tables. Ben and Rob or mortified, the rest of the table are loving it. A few of each of the other tables stand up and start giving it back to the Manchester infiltrators.

The bouncers stand up and look ready for a breakfast bar brawl.

Arkan then breaks the hostile atmosphere and shouts the

waiter. 'And a bottle each for that table,' he says, pointing to the Nottingham Forest home supporter table. 'And another for that table.'

The home tables settle to a murmur.

'Let's toast together, for a great game of football and may the best team win, thank you to Nottingham our hosts.' Arkan says.

As the tables all calm down and sit back in their seats, there is an uneasy calm.

The maître d' with a gaggle of waiting staff quickly bring out the ice buckets with the Cristal and serve the tables.

Frank raises a toast.

'To future partnerships and a great game of football.'

'Gëzuar,' rings out across the table.

As the group sit down and start their brunch, they smash down one glass of Champagne after another and order a full round of hot Bloody Mary shots. The conversations drift from football to immigration and they quiz Rob to see if his job or company could be useful to them and their new ventures. As brunch ends, Ben picks up the bill on his credit card. It's the first £1000++ breakfast he has ever encountered but he just smiles and takes the hit. Out of the corner of his eye he spots another one of the Stratford Haven Friday night club having brunch in the corner, Geoff. Ben's heart is in his throat. Geoff had been roped into one of Ben's Bitcoin 'investments'. He was in for £40k with the promise of big returns.

As the group leave the restaurant to the waiting Vito convoy, Ben edges round the room, deep in conversation with Rob, avoiding the gaze of Geoff. But it's no use. Geoff gets up and makes a B-line for Ben.

'Ben how are you?' he says.

'Hi, Geoff, sorry I didn't see you there.'

'All good?'

'Yes, thanks. You going to the game?'

'No, just having brunch with Felicity.' You going to the game?'

Ben breathes a small sigh of relief. 'Yes.'

'Who are the guys you're with, local mafia?' Geoff laughs.

'Ah, no, they are business associates; we are going to watch the reds; they need a win.'

'Right, how are we doing on the Bitcoin front?'

Ben's mouth goes dry, but he puts on a winning smile. 'All good, yes.'

'Have you managed to get the token sorted?'

'No, still sorting that. And I can't unlock anything until we get the token.'

'Right, I could do with the cash and the extra back ASAP, Ben.'

'Yes, understood. They're just trying to get the token unscrambled to release the cash. That's all.'

'How long?' Geoff pushes.

'Unsure at the moment, pal.'

'Alright, well, I'll be chasing you again. Ben, you know what I am saying don't you?'

'I get it," Ben says, swallowing hard. 'Leave it with me!'

'End of the week, send me an update,' Geoff says, tone turning to stone. 'And don't be a stranger, yeh?'

'Of course, Geoff. I'll sort this. Your money is safe.'

As Ben joins the group at the front of the building, he looks across the turning circle and spots a very large Mercedes G Wagon parked with two shady characters in gold rimmed sunglasses looking across at the group, window downplaying some heavy bass. The rear tinted windows drop down slowly, and Ben can see a character in the back lean forward, sucking hard on a Chupa Chups. The bodyguards step forward, but Arkan puts his hand up to pull the dogs back off their leashes. It's the Hyson Green Jamaican Yardies he has been expecting. He walks over slowly with the whole contingent, up to the rear window holding out his hand, puts it through the window and gives the guy in the back seat a gripped high five. The two are smiling and the atmosphere is convivial.

The other three in the car do not move off their eyes from

the rest of the Manchester gang, the entrance, and the rear-view mirrors. Skunk smoke seeps out through the front open windows and over the roof of the blacked-out G Class. The conversation only takes place for three or four minutes, and then the bouncers with holdalls meet one of the track suited and gold-chained passengers at the back door. The holdalls are dropped into the back of the G Wagon and the door is shut. The guy in the back hands an envelope to Arkan who tucks in his inside jacket pocket. They shake hands again, tinted windows go up trapping the cloud back in the car and they drive away at speed, bass pumping.

Ben looks to Frank. 'Who was that, Frank?'

'Just local business associates,' Frank says.

'What was in the holdalls?'

'Don't ask, Ben, it's better that you don't know.'

The Manchester group get into their waiting Vito's. The electric doors slide shut, and they work their way through Nottingham city and the football traffic. As they pull down Maid Marion way, one of the rowdy contingent pulls out a bottle of Raki and they pass it round, swigging from the bottle. Ben just looks out the window thinking this is going to be a long, 'challenging' day.

As they drive down London Road towards the ground, one of the groups shouts out, 'Hooters, Hooters! stop, stop!'

The group in the van all start laughing and cheering.

Ben looks at Arkan and says, 'I have somewhere booked already.'

'Pull up, pull up! Luan wants to see the Hooter girls! Don't worry my friend, we can drink here!'

The front Vito pulls into Hooters and the second follows. Ben had put Rob in the second Vito with all the Albanians. Rob got out holding his hands behind his head as if to say to Ben WTF!! Ben shrugs and points to the door.

'Come on Rob, it will be fine.' He gives Rob a wry smile. 'What can possibly go wrong!'

As it's match day, there are bouncers on the door, hands

stretched out, barring the group's entry. Arkan walks forward to talk to the bouncers. Whatever's said cannot be heard, but a wedge of cash is slipped into the bouncer's hand, and they gesture for the group to enter.

The group have seen US Hooters on TV back in Albania – it was a big thing. Ben enquires if they have a table. 'No tables todays sorry its match day,' comes the reply.

'I really need a table; can you help me? We won't be here long.'

'No, sorry,' the waitress says.

Ben reaches into his pocket. 'I really need a table. Will this help?' Ben pulls out a wad of twenty-pound notes.

'Hang on let me check with the manager.'

The waitress then walks over to the manager with the wedge of cash, and he nods and points over to a table.

They order buckets full of beer and a bottle of Grey Goose and more food. Ribs and chicken wings are delivered, family style and the group sits tearing at the meat, laughing, and staring. The group get up at various times in pairs and disappear off to the men's toilets, coming out rubbing their noses profusely and shaking their heads. It obvious it isn't the smell of the toilets that is bothering their senses. As the drinks flow, the men stare at the waitresses, some making inappropriate comments to the staff in Albanian.

The intoxicated group start singing a mixture of Man Utd and Albanian football chants and it is getting raucous. They are not even at the ground yet. As they leave the table of bones and empty bottles, Ben gets a call from the private club he had booked. They are furious as they have a prime table empty while waiting for the group. They have charged his credit card as agreed and taken the deposit in full. Ben remonstrates but without success. He had signed up and that was that – more cost.

Ben discreetly pays the bill and asks Frank to help heard the group out as they need to be at the box for 1.00pm latest. They are already late, and the group is rocking. As they get back in the Vito's the men are boisterous, opening the sliding sunroof and continue their signing and boozing as they smash back the Raki and glug from smuggled bottles of beer. They lean over and through the bus to crank up the music and both 'party buses' now make their way slowly towards the ground. It's quite a spectacle as they make their way through the slow-moving traffic over Trent bridge around to the executive suites at Forest. As they drive down over the bridge, they start throwing the bottles into the Trent. The drivers just look straight ahead and drive as this is what they are paid to do. They are clearly shitting themselves. The atmosphere is beyond tense, like a tinder box and one wrong word could send it up. They are swearing at the police and home supporters.

As they turn down Radcliffe Road, Arkan doesn't want to miss the match and with another one of the generals calms the group down. They sit up and listen immediately – like trained dogs to the whistle.

As they pull up to the car park at the back of the main stand you would think the last 15 minutes hadn't happened as both vans are peaceful. The group empties from the vans, tightening up their suit jackets adjusting their sunglasses. The bodyguards receive their orders from Arkan and walk to a nearby coffee shop once the group are safely through the turnstiles and inside the confines of the ground. Although they are not on their home turf, it will be known they are in the city, and it is less than safe to be walking around the city pissed.

The host welcomes the group into the hospitality area and states they can grab a quick drink before lunch is served in the next room. The gentlemen are very impressed with the female hosts who are polite, but it doesn't go unnoticed as to where the gaze of the group drifts to. As the Albanians try their best lines on the female hosts, Ben and particularly Rob just stand at the back of the group feeling very uncomfortable.

Once in the confines and safety of the ground, like a switch they turn back on the raucousness as they move to the bar area before they are seated into the box. They start throwing back the alcohol, ordering Ben to keep them coming, talking loudly in the bar, staring, or chatting up every female within 100 yards of them. The welcome bar is almost cleared, and the bar staff stare at them with their arms folded. Host staff then come over to the group and ask them again to take their seats in the hospitality suite before the game starts and they can go their box.

As the hosts throw open the doors to the large silent room, the speaker, an ex-Nottingham Forest footballer, is on the mike. No respect is shown as they cheer on entry and then loudly chat as they make their way to sit to at their table, knocking into other diners' chairs as they pass. All eyes are on the group as they are seated, Ben and Rob are mortified as they know some of the people in the room from the local boozer.

It's like a movie scene as this heavy set of outsiders move into position. Drinks are ordered and food arrives as they continue the football chat, the up-coming World Cup and whatever they want to talk about. Most of it is in Albanian so Ben and Rob can't keep up.

As the meal finishes, the group put their sunglasses and jackets back on, they are escorted to the box and take their seats for the game. Some complain to the host that the box is inside, not outside and that it is cheap and shitty inside. The host does not know how to respond and just smiles back and asks that they 'enjoy the game'. They order more drinks as the game kicks off to carry on their session. The host reminds them that drinks are at half time, and they cannot drink while the game is on. They kick off again, drawing the attention of the other boxes around them. Ben nervously gets up and leads the host out of the box. He negotiates to serve them red wine in coffee cups, paying off the hostess with another wedge.

Reluctantly, she agrees and puts two bottles of wine and 10 mugs in a cardboard box to refill, asking Ben to make sure he does it discreetly or she will be fired. Ben is just pleased they are inside as the group are banging on the glass, winding up the home crowd. Every United attack is raucously encouraged in the box much to the annoyance of the home supporters either side. By this point, Ben and Rob are at the limits of their alcohol capacity and are on the water. Frank is smashed, laughing, and encouraging the group to enjoy their day and drink as much as possible. As they continue their sesh, the game continues with a nil-nil draw at half-time. More booze flows and then heated debates back in the welcome bar. Home supporters either side of their box ask the group to calm down.

Friendly banter it may be, but the stewards speak to Ben, asking that he calms the group down or they may be asked to leave. Ben cannot risk this; it will go up in flames. The Manchester group are having none of it and United get on top and score two goals in the second half. It's now a powder keg. A little weary the Manchester contingent doesn't even bother leaving the box and take turns snorting lines on a bench at the back of the room through £50 notes. Ben looks to Frank for some sort of leadership, but Frank just smiles back and raises his coffee cup and shouts 'cheers'. It's totally out of control but Ben cannot do anything to stop it.

Rows and rows in front are watching the box not the game and the other boxes have turned, gesticulating to the Manchester box. Frank, who is supposed to be a Forest fan, and the Albanians do not give a shit and continue laughing, goading, and celebrating. Ben nips to the loo and stewards are gathered outside the box. It's getting very hostile. A little pissed, Ben slips into the toilet locks the toilet door and drops Lou a text.

Hi babe, how are you?
All good here are you ok?
Yes, all good, lively!!
What time are you back?
Not sure
Will you be back tonight?
Should be.
OK please be quiet as the twins will be asleep!

Will do, love you xx

As Ben slowly opens the door to urinals full of frustrated Forest fans, he quickly washes his hands and gingerly walks out into the corridor. There are now a large group of stewards and hosts hurriedly running about. Weirdly, the bodyguards are stood at the door smiling and talking, holding back the stewards. It turns out the muscle had bribed their way in after a call from Arkan. They are smiling and loving the chaos then a police officer comes to the group gathered at the door. Ben just stands back, rubbing his chin, totally out of his depth. Rob is in the room and will be shitting himself. Ben walks up and talks to the hosts to get himself back in and the bodyguards continue the conversation with the police who are asking politely if the group will calm down their enthusiasm if they want to get out unharmed or they will be ejected from the ground. As Ben opens the door, the group are all smiles and do not care one bit, even though they are surrounded by twenty-five thousand home fans. Rob has sunk into his chair, trying to blend into the furniture, praying a hole would just swallow him up. The group are all on their feet, clapping their hands and singing Manchester United songs, the adjoining boxes and most of the stand in front are now looking angrily at the group. Milkshake and chips covered in Gravy are slipping down the glass. The police are now down in the middle of the home supporters, remonstrating with them.

The police then come in with the chief steward and ask politely that the group chill out or they will have to leave, last warning. Arkan, like a chief UN negotiator, curbs the enthusiasm of the group and negotiates with the police and steward that they will be calm, enjoy the rest of the game and not cause a fuss. Arkan is very charismatic, fears nothing and works his magic.

The final whistle could not come soon enough. But exiting was Ben's real worry as they were now public enemy number one. As the game gets closer to finishing, Man United score again, minutes before the final whistle. The group just clap ironically.

Ben's hoping, they have drunk themselves into sobriety, but no, they are ready to go again. They watch the team celebrate on the pitch, the stand in front is emptying and the small group in front throw expletives and wanker signs to the group. They can hear shouting outside, banging on the walls and door. Ben and now Frank keeps the group talking while as many home supporters leave as possible. Frank knows the score and wants to enjoy the rest of the evening, being arrested is not a good look. As the group are shepherded out of the box and back towards the welcome bar, most of the hostile fans have left and Ben gets another round in. Rob is at the back of the group looking pale, slightly inebriated and shuffling with his head down trying to distance himself from the group.

'You ok, Rob?' Ben asks.

'Yes, all good, just not feeling 100%.'

'Have you heard all you need and happy with the investment?'

'Yes, I have seen all I need to. Are you confident with where this is going?'

'100% confident in the business plan and it's a sound investment. The group have been a little lively letting off steam. Apparently, it's been a busy week in Manchester.' Ben forces a smile.

'Yes, lively, that's one word for it Ben.'

'It will all be good; you have my word.'

'OK, I am putting 100% trust in you to get this investment right and get my money back and the agreed profit.'

'You have my word; I haven't let you down before, have I?'

'Well, apart from the other £50k that will need paying back,' Rob says, laughing awkwardly.

'Yes, yes, no problem. It's all rolled in, we are priced in, don't worry Rob!'

'Ok, agreed, but it's down to you, mate.'

'Trust me,' Ben says with a wink.

Ben gives Rob a big hug. 'I will be in touch next week, see you next Friday down the pub.'

The group don't even notice Rob has left. Ben takes a massive intake of breath and walks back to the bar area when the group complete with bodyguards are stood around the table talking loudly. Frank's eyes are all over Ben.

'Is he OK?' Frank asks.

'Yes, all good.'

'And the money?'

'Yes, all agreed.'

'So, we can set up the transfer as agreed?'

'Yes, we can to the agreed dates.' Ben pauses. 'Frank, if these guys are doing so well, why do they need our cash?'

Frank pulls Ben away from the group by his arm. 'You don't ask questions, right?'

'Right, but if business is so good....'

'It is but we have multi projects and we cannot get the cash out of the 'other' business quick enough.'

Ben knew this meant laundering cash quick enough.

'We have to move the cash carefully and slowly for all the right reasons do you understand?' Frank hisses.

'Yes, sure.'

'We don't ask questions. The new businesses will take time to replace the turnover. I am not telling you too much more as you know too much already. It's for your own good. You understand the consequences don't you, Ben?'

'Consequences?'

'If this goes pear shaped or anything that I have told you gets out and comes back to you or any of your associates, then it doesn't end well.'

'Frank, you can trust me you know that.'

'It's not me that needs to trust you.'

As Ben peers over Frank's shoulder, he catches Arkan's gaze who is talking to one of the bodyguards and nods back at Ben.

Ben is way out of his depth but now too far in. Ben and Frank round up the group back to the Vito's and they sing 'glory,

glory Man United' down the steps to the exit. Ben quickly nods at the drivers to get the doors open. The bodyguards stand, arms folded, staring intimidatingly at any Forest fans left. Ben points towards the vans and herds them in one by one. Ben breathes a sigh of relief and directs the vans back into the safety of the crowds back in town, towards the Cosy Club where they have a discrete VIP table on their own out the way so this group can continue into oblivion.

As they arrive at the club, Arkan clears out the van to ensure it is just Ben, Frank and another guy that calls himself the commercial director, Roan. Ben is set for a grilling.

'Ben you all good for the investment?' Arkan asks.

'Yes, all good,' Ben says.

'And the 3-stage payments, no delays.' Arkan adds. 'Why did you friend leave?'

'Not feeling well.'

'He is involved in this.'

'Yes, a silent partner.'

'Silent. He knows what silence is, yes. I've not given him details; he just thinks he's investing in me.'

'What about you. Do you know the code?' Arkan puts his finger to his lips sssssshhhhhhh. 'If this goes how you say, 'tits up', you are 'no comment.'

'Yes, sure Arkan, you can trust me!' Ben says.

Arkan turns to Frank. 'You trust him?'

'He knows the rules of the game, Arkan.'

'That's good, Ben.'

Arkan brings his hand to his face, spits into is hand and holds it out to Ben.

If Ben wasn't sure what he'd signed up for, he was now. The confrontational nature of his new business partners has made it clear that this gang need to be kept sweet. It is clear what the consequences would be if his contract, now shook on, wasn't completed to the Arkan's satisfaction.

Chapter 11

The Line Has Been Crossed

The twins traumatic birth changed everything. Ben was lost and the first person he turned to was Lou's sister, Hetty. It had to be family as the other girls at work didn't want to hear about his woes.

Hetty was more up to date than any of the family or friends as Ben and Hetty continued their text conversations, but it now was more in depth and in detail and feelings were involved. Ben was reaching out. Hetty started to become more protective over Ben as the story of the birth night unfolded. The texts got more loving and although they used to sign off with a xx now it was hugging and kiss blowing emojis. When Ben came home while Lou was still in hospital, after seeing Jake and Megan his next port of call was Hetty on his own.

He wanted it to be somewhere private for coffee where he could offload his woes to a familiar face. He chose the quietest biggest coffee shop he could think off.

Ben was having a cigarette outside, pacing the pavement. Hetty walked up, looking stunning in her work attire. As she approached, they both embraced and, as the tears flowed down both their cheeks, they both clung to each other like limpets. Ben let it all out like he was meeting his soulmate. Eventually, they prized apart entered the coffee house where Ben talked through everything, opening a flood gate about all his feelings, his fears, and his worries for Lou.

These coffee meetings became a regular occurrence over the years, around family and social events. Hetty was Ben's confidant, councillor, friend, and his other partner.

As the twins made their way past their 5th and 6th birthdays, things became a little more serious. Meeting at their regular coffee shop, they discussed Phil and how bored Hetty was. Ben gave his usual cheery, funny, and alternative view of how life could be for Hetty with another fella or him, each alternative jokingly, not jokingly involved Ben. It really cheered up Hetty and she was laughing and going along with Ben's talk about how she could spice up her relationship with affairs. Ben listened intently when Hetty talked of her attraction to certain women. She explained that she had a type which intrigued and excited Ben. He probed further, fantasising about a threesome, but obviously not with Lou.

As they got up to walk out of the café, Ben was overcome with thoughts of where this could go for him and, not quite knowing what he was doing, in the middle of the café, he pulled back from his goodbye hug with Hetty and kissed her full on the lips. Hetty's heart was jumping all over the place and she melted into the kiss for a few seconds, savouring the moment before she pulled back.

'Ben, no.'

'Sorry, Hetty. I couldn't resist.'

'Ben, we mustn't.'

'Sorry Hetty, sorry. I am just so confused about what to do next. Lou and I are going nowhere, and I need to be close to someone.'

'Ben, we will get through this I am here for you, but this is wrong.'

Ben put his arm around Hetty, and they left together,

walking towards the car park. He has to go to home for a social services appointment at home with Lou and the twins.

Arrive at their cars, like awkward teenagers they look each other in the eyes and kiss again but this time its full on. Soft and tender, this is just what Ben needed – to feel close and affectionate with someone to give him a vision of what the future might hold. Could he be the supportive husband and father but have his sexual needs met by a lifelong target?

Hetty was cut in half, this was a lifetime of waiting to be close to Ben like this and how could she do this to her sister. They had crossed the line, and there was no going back. As they kissed for what felt like a lifetime, Hetty pulled back. Ben's eyes slowly opened as the world around them stood still.

'What are we going to do, Hetty?'

Hetty paused. 'Ben, I just don't know, but Lou cannot not know about this. It just wouldn't be fair on her, you know how she is at the moment.'

'I know Hetty but...'

'We need to give this time,' she said.

'Hetty, can we meet again?'

'Concentrate on the twins, Megan, Jake, and Lou for now and let's talk later. I need to process this.'

Aroused by events, Ben floats back to the car. He fumbles for his keys as he glances back at Hetty. It felt wrong but so right.

Hetty is torn, she has what she always wanted and captured 'her man' and got one up on Lou, which all felt incredibly wrong in the circumstances. She slumps in the car and looks in the rear-view mirror, unable to look herself in the eye. It was wrong, wrong, wrong and she knew it, but Ben was her first crush and so opposite to Phil. Could she have both? Weird thoughts race through her mind. What does this say about me? This is my brother-in-law and it's my sister!! As she starts the car her mobile pings.

Thank you Hetty that really helped and sorry for the kiss

I could not resist, and I really want to spend more time with you. XX

Hetty stares at the phone for a few seconds and deletes the text, she could not risk this text being seen by Phil by mistake.

All of their meetings before this had been flirty and touchy, but this was a different level.

Hetty knew this would blow their worlds apart. She went back to work on a weird high, sexually charged, and could not stop thinking about Ben – her emotions were all over the place.

Over the next few weeks, the texts flowed back and forth between Ben and Hetty, getting more detailed and more honest about how they felt about each other. They switched to Snapchat, so their explicit messages disappeared into the ether.

Hetty started to make more effort with her sister, guilt seeping into her insides. Ben agreed this was a good idea, adding to the deceit.

They kept their coffee rendezvous here and there. Hetty would blow hot and cold with Ben which drove him mad and kept him wanting more. He was always ready to go straight to the car and drop into a country lane, book into a hotel, or go away together. He had always been driven by his trousers. Hetty set the pace and the boundaries but was falling for Ben.

They were always discrete and careful, ensuring where they met was off the family and friend patch. They kissed, they held each other, and Ben talked mostly about his fears for the future, the twins 'changing' behaviours and physical changes but, mainly about he and Hetty moving forward together.

Ben was intent on going well beyond an illicit 'coffee meet' affair. It would mean breaking Lou's trust in him forever and leave Hetty's relationship with her sister and family beyond repair.

Ben saw a lot of it as collateral damage on the pathway to a new life beyond, either with Lou and the children and Hetty or with Hetty alone. Frankly, he was not interested in the fall out.

Hetty, doing her own impact assessment, was less convinced saying there was no way back once this came out. She needed to buy time to formulate an explanation and contingency plan.

Lou saw an unstable future with Ben caring for the twins with all the energy they could muster, watching Jake and Megan flourish and being family as a unit held together by gaffer tape. She had no idea that Ben's mind was drifting elsewhere – Lou, family, and a new life with a Hetty, an attractive, younger version of his wife. Hetty also was financially well off, owned a house, had money, and had a good job with prospects. Hetty ignored the fact that maybe, just maybe, Ben might be doing it for the money.

There was undoubtedly a deep connection. They had known each other along time from schooldays and Hetty could not get away from the fact that they were now an unofficial couple.

Following the rendezvous, Hetty always came away floating above the ground she had helped Ben and made him feel more confident about the future, in turn giving Lou a more supportive partner. She finally had that spark in her life. This floaty feeling often made it easy to ignore how this was going to blow their worlds apart when the truth was outed.

Ben made her laugh; they had fun and although couldn't be with their friends as a couple, they met in busy locations with built in alibis. On their 'coffee meets' when their paths did cross with friends or associates, they would just cheerily pass it off as 'just a coffee' talking about the twins and how much Hetty was helping her sister. They both knew it felt wrong, it felt exciting, and the next obvious step was a to meet up for sex.

Hetty was not ready for this.

Chapter 12
A Trip to the Lakes

Hetty had got into lending Ben money behind Phil's back, spending savings and getting out loans in her name to support him. She was cash rich and had no mortgage, Ben knew this.

Her lines of credit were drying up. Ben was really falling for Hetty, and she was feeling the same. The more they talk about the future, the more Hetty started to believe it could happen.

Ben couldn't see a pathway out of for his family and financial situation, so he dialled up all his attention towards Hetty. He was falling in love with what he was familiar with – you cannot get closer to the same thing as sisters after all. In his deepest, darkest thoughts, Ben saw that Hetty would clear the debts his debt, came with no emotional baggage and he could get back to where he started with Lou – pre-kids. Loving times when they were free to do what they wanted without children but, more importantly, without the relentless care regime. Hetty was a highly sexual being, dominant and confident and someone that Ben was incredibly sexually attracted to. She had been very explicit in her desires, and it drove Ben insane.

Ben knew it was selfish but deep-down he just did what he wanted so could justify it until the cows came home. His relationship with Hetty though would be the final nail in his marriage coffin and would alienate all of this family and split his friends. Lou was struggling and most of her friends and family had not come through to help so it was more to Ben's benefit to set up the news in his favour and support Lou where he could.

In the early days of the twins being born, Ben had strayed at work with younger members of his and other teams. He had a type; young, impressionable ambitious females that looked up to him. Ben craved attention and appreciated female company a little bit too much. He worked hard to find the right females and then 'Love bombed' them. Ben was fun to be around, the all-round good time boy. Loved a drink, the odd line of coke, an E and would be first and last at the party. The directors had spotted this and that gave him the reputation of a being a bit of a loose cannon, holding him back in the corporate world. But Ben was oblivious to this. There were work trips away and dinners where he stepped over the line with younger members of company, but it was passed off, he managed to get through a disciplinary for a relationship that had gone wrong, and the ingrained misogynistic environment covered his arse for him. Ben's victim left shortly after; it knocked him but didn't stop him. He just became more careful in his selection process. Ben was not always honest about his marriage and didn't wear a wedding ring or have any photos of his family around him, Lou would rarely get involved in any work events after the kids were born. On the whole, it was usually consensual, and Ben just couldn't resist – if there was a naughty connection Ben was in like Flynn. He was always careful that it would never get home to Lou. There was never any firm evidence of his indiscretions and only a few people had an idea of what Ben was up to.

His various work affairs had helped Ben build up a tolerance against the guilt he should have felt.

His need and want for attention amplified after the twins

were born. It went right back to a young boy's need for his mother's love and, for Ben, this had morphed into the need for all female attention as he grew up. If there was someone of interest to Ben in the office, he would go to any lengths to get what he wanted. Basically, a cad but, a careful cad going to great lengths to hide his illicit affairs, with the help of his burner phone. Although unable to resist the temptations around him, Ben's underlying desire was never to hurt Lou or the children. In some twisted way, Ben wanted both sisters in his life and no change. To have his cake and eat it.

Things had got steamy between Ben and Hetty, but always a controlled steamy. Hetty was careful and measured with how far they took it but there was a looming sense of inevitability every time they met. Ben was constantly suggesting a night away, Hetty knew this was massive as it not only was wrong but also had consequences on the twins' care, Jake and Megan and was the ultimate betrayal. Hetty felt they could get away with maybe what they had been up to already, but sex and a night away was a whole different level. Ben had his eyes on the perfect location in the lakes – a couple of hours away. Two separate cars and weeks of planning... They didn't know anyone in the lakes. Ben had picked up that the Watergate Bay Hotel in Cornwall, site of many of his family holidays as a child, had opened another boutique hotel in the Lakes and it was a perfect spot. This secluded location allowed them total anonymity and time away together in a beautiful location. Ben mentioned it over and over again on their secret meets, finally Hetty succumbed and agreed a date.

*

Phil was on a stag trip (which he hated) with old mates. Ben knew he needed a watertight story for Lou to excuse himself for one night of support caring. It would be a Saturday night, so Ben concocted a story that Uncle Frank's associates in Manchester were having a night out to celebrate getting planning permission on the new development. Ben needed to be there to show face and ensure they knew he was good for the money (which he wasn't). Ben was already in for £30k to help break ground at the new site. Lou was annoyed, asking why he had to be away for the whole weekend and could not just go for just the night and drive back the next morning. Ben explained there were plans and financials to work on, pushing the story as far as him imagination would take him. Ben even paid for the caring agency to lay on extra staff for the weekend, above and beyond to allow him to spend this time away.

Reluctantly, Lou agreed. All Ben wanted to do was spend as much time as he could with Hetty and away from the relentless caring duties.

As the date got closer and closer, the texts between Hetty and Ben became more frequent and Ben more gushing and explicit. Hetty was racked with guilt but the allure of the weekend and time with Ben to take this relationship to the next level was a prospect she was secretly excited about. As the week of the weekend approached, they didn't have their usual meet up. The Friday came and Ben drifted into the garden for a cigarette and a fired a text off covered in hug and kisses emojis explaining what time he would be there. As they signed off, they both went to sleep that night thinking about the weekend and what was about to transpire.

Ben got up as normal and helped Lou with the caring duties until the carers came for their allotted time. Holding back any sign that he was going for an enjoyable weekend away, Ben carefully packed his business smart casual gear in his suit holder and leather bag. Megan and Jake were picked up early for sports clubs, so this just left Ben to say goodbye to the twins and Lou. Lou was manoeuvring the Ted and Holly in their equipment and without even looking up said, 'goodbye.'

Ben said 'kiss' and Lou glanced up and with pursed lips just pecked him on the cheek. Ben knowing, he was doing wrong turned, desperately trying not to smile, and left for the door throwing his suit bag over his shoulder. Walking away Ben mutters 'Love you' as he walks through the door looks back, breathing a sigh of relief. For a brief moment, it's like looking back at somebody else's life on TV. This still doesn't feel like the new reality and closing the door is like turning off the TV. It always felt more like somebody else's life and Ben found it easy to slip out of his new life, much easier than Lou who was never comfortable leaving the family home or being far from the twins. As Ben pulls out the drive, the enormity of this illicit tryst creates a huge shot of adrenaline, shooting through his body like a drug. Ben drops a quick text to Hetty – 'on way' – shuffles through his playlist and selects The Smiths 'This Charming Man' and he is off. As he is driving, he gets a quick reply from Hetty 'same xx'.

The geography changes from Nottinghamshire to South Yorkshire and eventually Cumbria. His chosen location, Another Place in Ullswater, is close and his excitement rises. Ben had booked the Joules suite – dark and sultry with great views across the Ullswater.

Ben parks the car outside the whitewashed and slate-roofed stately home. He checks in and makes his way up the dark walnut stairs, past vintage artifacts up to the room. He has a smile on his face and is walking at pace to ensure the room is exactly right and wants to set the scene.

Slowly opening the door, he thinks to himself – perfect; classy and sultry. His pulse is racing, mouth dry as he anticipates Hetty's arrival. His mind is racing at how it will play out. How long can he make the foreplay last, what it will be like when they first touch. He thinks about the feeling of the penetration and how warm and satisfying it will be. How many times will he be able to make love? He thinks about the undoing her bra and cupping her pert breasts for the first time and sucking her nipples. He goes to the bathroom unpacks his wash bag , washes his knob, brushes his teeth, and leaves the bathroom neat and tidy for Hetty, unpacks his case, plugs in his charger, looks out of the window, and then sinks into the sofa.

Hetty arrives at the location full of guilt. *What am I doing,* she thinks, *this is wrong, should I turn round and go back. Should I resist the temptation and just say no. We could just sleep in the same room and not do anything – couldn't we?*

Once she lets this happen there is no going back. Her heart is racing and although she knows this is a cardinal sin, has waited for this moment with Ben all of her life. She sits in the car, radio on listening to her Chick Flicks favourite – Hey Baby - staring out across Ullswater and the small boats bobbing up and down.

It's a beautiful spot, as Hetty breathes in deeply, she texts Ben.

Are you here?
Yes, ask the Joules room first floor turn right at the top of the stairs, are you here?
Yes
OK see you in a bit. Xxxxxxxx

Hetty puts her hands on the steering wheel and looks down, getting the strength to block out the thoughts of what's about to happen – a few minutes pass as Hetty looks up at the view, her phone and closing her eyes.

She turns off the music, opens the door and gets her overnight bag from the boot and looks at the building in front of her, in the back of her mind praying no one she knows is there. She smiles at reception and walks up the ornate stairs to the room. She knocks on the room door labelled the Joules Suite and Ben slowly opens the door.

'Hi babe!' he says with a grin.

'Hi,' she says quietly.

'How are you doing? How was the traffic?'

'Fine. I am OK. Ben... Ben, what are we doing?'

Ben launches straight into it. 'Hetty, I have fallen for you and have always wanted us to be together.'

'Ben you cannot say that.'

'But Hetty I do.'

Ben takes Hetty's bag and drops it to the floor. Taking hold of her hands, he pulls her towards him. 'Hetty, we have this moment together I need you. I want us to be together.'

'What about the kids, Ben, and the twins?'

'We will work that through.'

She pauses and then whispers, 'What about Lou?'

'Let's not talk about Lou, this is about me and you.'

Hetty is tearful, struggling to cope with her emotions.

'Hetty, I need you and I know you want me.'

Ben leans forward, let's go of Hetty's hand and wipes away her tears. Cupping her chin, he looks deeply into her eyes and kisses her. They kiss passionately for what seems like forever, holding each other closely as if they cannot let go. Ben gently pushes Hetty backwards until she is against the dark walnut desk. Ben lifts Hetty up by her thighs, her skirt riding up her muscular legs, and places her on the desk. They continue to kiss, and Ben gently pushes up Hetty's skirt until her powder blue Agent Provocateur knickers are visible. Ben undoes her cream blouse, revealing a cream bra, her breasts spilling over the top. As Ben looks down, he cannot resist moving his hand onto Hetty's see through knickers, pressing gently through the fabric. Hetty arches her back as Ben starts to stroke her through her knickers. Hetty cannot resist and is breathing heavily. Ben knows that this is the moment. He pulls the powder blue knickers down slowly, Hetty grips both sides of Ben's head and pushes it down. She writhes in ecstasy as she pushes Ben's head down. Hetty is arched against the dresser's mirror, clearly in charge of what's going to happen next. As Hetty reaches orgasm, she squirts all over Ben's face and he loves it. As he looks up, Hetty meets his gaze, confident and as he looks past her cream bra at her beautiful eyes, they smile at each other. Ben slowly rises up and, as he does, he removes her silky cream blouse and pings open her bra, her pert breast pop out. Ben cannot resist, running his tongue over each breast. Hetty slowly pushes him off, removes her skirt, licks her fingers, and walks across the room. She drapes herself across the green couch, looking sultrily back at Ben as she pleasures herself. Ben quickly undresses, his erect cock bouncing out of his boxers, and he walks towards her. She pulls his cock into her mouth, one hand returning to pleasuring herself. Ben stokes Hetty's soft hair, losing himself in her vigorously pleasuring him.

Before he explodes, Hetty stops, looks at Ben and moves him away. She stands over the end of the sofa and then bending down slowly. Her pert buttocks and muscular are body taught and ready for him. He gently asks, 'is this, ok?' and then positions himself behind her while she looks back at him. He penetrates Hetty slowly and forcefully. She moans in pleasure and so does Ben. This is the moment they have been waiting for and it's amazing. Ben thrusts from behind as Hetty's nails dig into the soft velour of the pea green sofa and her head is arched back. Ben thrusts faster and faster and as he does, she turns her head and releasing her grasp Hetty, with one hand pushes Ben out of her. Turning round, perched on the end of the sofa she wraps her legs around him and positions his cock back inside her. Ben looks down at her pert breasts bouncing backwards and forwards as he pumps her and as he does, Hetty pushes up with her pelvic floor and Ben grabs her thighs, pulling her in and out. Hetty's eyes are closed but Ben wants to watch their bodies together. Hetty works out a lot and keeps her weight down, she is muscular and athletic. Ben cannot contain himself and as he comes close to climax Hetty's eyes prize open, and she lurches for Ben's cock. She grabs hold between the head and the shaft and squeezes sharply. Ben has never experienced anything like this before. Ben asks if Hetty is, ok? She presses her fingers against his lips. Her fingers smell of sex. The need to orgasm disappears and Hetty starts to masturbate Ben until he is hard again. She moves Ben to the bed and climbs on top of him. Ben takes some time starting again but Hetty makes all the right noises and nibbles his ear. As he starts to get close to climax again, Hetty almost telepathically knows and pushes Ben out of her and squeezes his shaft again until the need to release disappears. Ben cannot believe this. He has never seen or felt anything like this before. Getting himself hard again, Hetty slowly moves onto all fours, Ben gripping her hips as he moves in and out of her from behind. Hetty screams in ecstasy as she pleasures herself and Ben pumps her. This time, when Ben reaches point of climax, she turns round and lays back. Ben explodes over Hetty's breasts and it's a level of pleasure he has never felt before. It seems to go on forever. As they both collapse onto the bed, Hetty pulls Ben in and they cuddle, the animal scent of sex and cum between them. They cannot stop kissing each other. This has been a long time coming and they are both lost in their own world. This feels real and this feeling for both is not going to go away.

They talk, go for a walk around the grounds. Have dinner together, drink a lot of wine – a lot. The make love through the night and cannot keep their hands off each other. They eventually fall asleep. As Ben wakes, he looks over at Hetty's beautiful face, clear complexion, and soft features. Hetty wakes sometime later and looks over to Ben.

'Morning,' he whispers, kissing her on the forehead.

'Morning, Ben.' She can't help but smile.

'How's your head?'

'Rough.' She laughs. 'How about you?'

'I feel great, Hetty.' Ben says earnestly.

'What are we going to do Ben?'

'I don't know. Let's see how it goes when we get back, but Hetty I really want to keep this going until we find a way. Last night was simply incredible.'

Hetty looks away as she knows it's wrong, but absolutely adores Ben and, he's right, this has been amazing.

'I am going to take a shower,' she says.

'OK.'

Ben watches Hetty get out of the bed, the sheets falling off her lithe body towards the shower. Ben pops a Viagra and lays in bed surveying the crime scene, recalling each area of the room they had managed to shag on or in. As time passes, he starts to become aroused. He hears the shower come on. Thinking of Hetty, he's almost instantly stiff and he gets up and walks to the shower. He stands in awe of Hetty in the shower, she looks so beautiful. He opens the shower door and runs his fingers down he muscular back. Hetty turns, smiles, and they start to kiss. He lifts Hetty's lithe legs up around his waist and they make love for one last time. It is wet and wild, putting a full stop on this 24 hour of passion before they go back to normality. As they dry each other off, they talk about home. All Ben is interested in is when can they meet again, this has been a mind-blowing weekend, for Hetty is about damage limitation and trying to get best outcomes all round for what will be World War 3 for the families.

After breakfast, they walk hand in hand around the lake. Ben turns to Hetty and tells her he thinks he loves her. Hetty looks down and reluctantly says she feels the same. Hetty then turns to kiss Ben and thanks him for an amazing weekend and that they must do right by Lou and the children. Ben and Hetty agree not to break this news yet and want to hold this down until they both lay the foundations and agree a plan. They walk back to the hotel; the bags are already packed and in the car. They stop turn to each other and kiss and then with a 'drive safely' are away. This cannot be undone; the feelings are too deep. It has been a romantic time bomb, years in the making and it's gone off – big time.

Chapter 13

Tribunal Trauma

A failed attempt at an educational tribunal to get the twins into a weekday residential placement meant the kids were at home full time. Ben and Lou had fought for an EHC plan (Education, Health, and social plan) and an SEN (Statement of Educational Needs) for each twin. They had no idea why they needed it or what it was, but it was essential and would give them a multi-agency plan to access additional support and an appropriate education. The social area was wafer thin almost giving them nothing. On the education side, the local primary school said they could accommodate the twins which Ben and Lou were highly sceptical of. When Lou went around the school, they were literally just in a class at the back with both twins sharing a teaching assistant who hadn't even been recruited or trained at the time of the visit. Ben dropped off the case, leaving Lou, who he would often state 'was at home all week' to do it all on her own. Lou felt a huge amount of pressure steering her way through this uncharted territory, dealing with Education, Health and Social. These organisations were behemoths, well administered, well-resourced and most importantly they knew what they were doing. Lou was an organisation of one and had no experience – it was a minefield and an incredibly challenging time trying to maintain the household schedule, care regime and a marriage. Friends and family were well down the agenda although Lou did try, but the latest knock-back from social care wasn't a great conversation starter, so she battled alone. When Ben was listening, Lou would share her thoughts and fears, trying to vent and feel less along, but he just wanted outcomes and would often say Lou 'Ok, what's the solution?' as if he was at work. It pissed Lou off as she often didn't have a solution, she wasn't a social worker or a law expert! Lou's upbringing meant she felt the need to know all the answers, driven by her parents, so these new layers of law and administration were incredibly frustrating to deal with. She often sat opposite a panel or an individual trying to argue a point with zero experience against a group of highly trained, highly deflective specialists whose job was to give you the absolute minimum or, ideally, nothing. Nothing was a win.

Lou realised very quickly it's all about money and no matter how many tears are shed with these individuals, how many tales of woe you wove, they didn't bat an eyelid. Over time, Lou got to understand how the panel, or the individuals worked. The minute you showed weakness, lack of knowledge or frustration they fed off it and you would lose. It was a game of attrition. Ben was no use as he would steam in and even start to berate the panel individuals – once this happened you had lost. These people were very skilled at what they did with a clear agenda. Some of the panels they sat on there were two exasperated, knackered, and frustrated parents versus 18 skilled individuals.

The Educational Tribunal to get the children into a social needs residential primary school was perfect for the children. It was in Hampshire, so the children would be picked up by special needs transport and taken to the school on a Monday and brought back on a Friday. They also offered short stay respite. When Ben and Lou visited, they were visually moved by the facility, staff, and the smiles on the children's faces. It gave the children there all they need, physio support, education, hydrotherapy, occupational therapy, speech and language therapy, nursing support, peer group and most importantly, friends. It wasn't cheap, though, and the battle started as soon as they exposed their wishes to send the twins together to the school. Lou had to learn how to apply for a tribunal to decide. It was the parents versus the authority. Megan and Jake heard the many conversations and frustration between Ben and Lou regarding this process. It added to Jake's hatred of authority and what the twins brain injury had brought down onto the family and what Jake blamed for the breakdown of his relationship with Lou.

Jake was first born and had a great relationship with both mum and dad. Funny and outgoing, he was such a mummy's boy but after the arrival of his sister and then the twins Jake had gone through a lot for someone so young. It changed him.

Jake was sporty and fiercely competitive at pre-school and primary school. The arrival of his sister Megan exacerbated this and the sibling rivalry between Megan and Jake took hold as soon as his sister got her voice. Megan idolised her brother when she was little but after two and half became a real match for Jake. Megan had a real steely competitive streak in her – Lou claimed it was directly inherited from her side of the family.

Throughout Jake's early years, he was top of his class. Supported by his athletic dad, his sporting achievement was a huge part of their early life together. Cricket, football, rugby, and golf – anything with a bat, stick, club, or ball. Jake took to all of it like a duck to water, a natural sportsman and young leader, the mirror of his dad's early years at school. Having mum and dad cheering him on the side lines was a permanent fixture.

The build-up to the twins being born and the excitement of a brother and sister was the height of anticipation. Ben, Lou, Jake, and Megan would often sit around talking about the lovely things they would be doing together with their new brother and sister. Playing together, teaching them to play the sports Megan and Jake loved, camping trips, holidays. All the plans, cheerful conversions about the future all gone in a heartbeat.

The events of the fateful night and the twins' brain damage had a dramatic and profound effect on Jake. He had been told he was the man of the house and took it literally in his dad's absence. Jake didn't quite understand what this meant and thought it meant taking on the responsibility for the whole family, Guilt seeped into Jake's soul, he felt as though he had let that night happen because he wasn't there, like a die-hard football fan who puts down a loss to their absence at the grounds. He would listen to mum and dad's endless conversations and caring hours spent with the twins and he took in every word. The negligence claim, the characters on the maternity ward that night, the frustrations of living with the multi-agency input – Jake took it all on himself. It seemed like he aged 5 years in 12 months and became like a little old man.

Attention shifted from Jake and Megan to the twins overnight and their all-consuming care regime was put at the centre of everything. As this the eldest, Jake felt it more than his sister. The equipment got bigger and more noticeable as the twins grew older and Jake was hypersensitive when they were out and about, fully aware of the eyes on them, the sniggers, and the pointing. Jake would shrink as small as he could or hide behind the buggy. His home situation was kept from as many as possible at school to maintain his leadership of the groups and sports teams. He knew he would be ridiculed relentlessly by the older boys if they knew his brother and sisters were disabled. Jake reeled at the jokes, social media posts and belittling of disabled children and adults. He would hide his anger and just smile. Never got involved but never challenged as to not be seen as they odd one out. There were children with mild disabilities at his school and they were bullied for their walk, perceived lack of intelligence or the way they talked or looked. Even the short-sighted were ridiculed relentlessly. It was a Lord of the Flies environment with teachers not encouraging this elitist and cruel behaviour but also not curbing it or educating the ignorant that their actions were not acceptable in this day and age. At one point, Jake sat in a large group of the rugby lads, a lot were older doing their Duke of Edinburgh awards and school volunteering at a local special school and adult disability group. Jake spent the hour cringing and with his stomach in knots as they ridiculed the disabled people they were there to help. Others were sharing their social media videos of disabled people being filmed for being disabled. It was excruciating for Jake and a moment he never forgot.

As Jake stepped through year 7, his behaviour took a dramatic change. Jake hit puberty and Boom. Overcome with new emotions and feelings, he felt incredibly self-conscious of his own looks and how the twins were perceived by society. His emotions felt like a freight train with no driver careering down the tracks – mood swings with massive highs and lows. Jake was struggling to sleep, not keeping up with his homework and was becoming more and more reclusive.

His participation in sport was dropping off and Jake found himself not being picked for the first team. Gaming and more insular social media activities took over. Jake was on his devices well into the night with doors and curtains closed.

Jake wasn't keen on family trips out, wasn't so keen on having friends over and his friendship group was shrinking. The football, rugby and cricket party invites had gone from what seemed like every weekend to almost non-existent. Lou was full on with care and dad was not where he should be, so they didn't notice. Jake simply slipped through the cracks, forgotten, and ignored.

It was now distancing as Lou focused on this new battle. It was a full year end to end from when the children were four and half years old. They were almost five and half by the time it came to the tribunal. The special school had provided an advocate, Sheena, to help Ben and Lou but legal support was financial out of reach. They had enquired but could expect a £100,000 bill. This was out of the question. The head of the school, Alistair, would attend the tribunal but that was it. Ben and Lou were on their own.

As the day of the tribunal came, Lou did everything she could get the evidence they needed from the school physio, education, occupational therapy, speech and language, nursing, reports made up a huge bundle. As they entered the court building, they were met by the team for the defence.

'My god,' Lou whispered – they had brought nine education, health, and social experts to fight the parents. They had also employed a barrister and two solicitors. Lou was beside herself.

'We've lost, Ben.' She sighed.

The advocate tried to reassure them that the 'independent' panel would be impartial. As they sat in the room, Lou and Sheena were faced by a panel of three. One from social, education and health and two note-takers. Lou and Sheens fought hard to represent the children, Lou had brought pictures of the twins to try and personalise this horrific process. The panel were stern, professional, and very intimidating. It was a cold, soulless process.

The panel challenged their reasoning and the authority put together a very convincing but thin on evidence argument. There was a lot not in place and they worked hard to convince all would be in place for the start of term in the local mainstream school, including building a toilet block and changing area for the twins. A lot of the evidence they brought had not been shared pre-tribunal so Lou and Sheena struggled to argue that it wouldn't be in place. The barrister for the authority shot holes in the residential school, the reports they had created and their record. There was absolutely no evidence to their allegations but all they needed was to put doubt in the panel's mind. They got into the weeds of the detail and every word or statement they had from Lou and the school. They also stated that Ben and Lou were overzealous, demanding, character assassinating them both with the precision of a sniper.

Lou and Ben found this incredibly hard, and Ben had to leave the room twice to punch the wall – he was so angry that the very authority there to protect and care could be so fucking heartless and cold. There were breaks where the panel asked both sides to leave the room. Only Sheena and the Alistair were allowed to stay to hear the closed arguments, leaving Ben and Lou huddled in a corner drinking rank coffee. Sheena and Alistair tried to put on a brave face but the barristers acting for the authority were wiping the floor with them both. After all, they were an advocate and a head just trying to offer the best they could for the children they educated. The barrister and authority were there to win and did this every day – they knew exactly which buttons to press and pressed them hard. The cost difference over a year to educate and care for the twins ran into hundreds of thousands at the residential school compared to the state school.

The afternoon tribunal session was centred around the social care element, and the head of social care worked hard to convince the panel that the state school could meet all the needs the residential school could. She threatened that if they did go to the residential school out of county that they could no longer provide any care. All within the law and rules the local authority had set themselves! Sheena worked hard to explain that the residential school provided the 24-hour care needed for the twins. The authority argued they didn't need 24/7 care the health and physio element were a huge element of the waking day curriculum for the twins and the school were experts in this area. The authority argued that health could meet the need and a Physio would attend the school once every 8 weeks and that was all the twins required. Speech and Language therapy would be provided on a rota every 6 weeks and the twins would be in a group session. The residential school argued it needed to be part of the everyday curriculum with hourly sessions each week to give the twins the very best chance in the future. The Authority argued this was overkill and not required, it was a gold standard, and they were not here to agree a gold standard. It wouldn't be the best use of public money.

As 3pm approached, two of the authority team asked to leave to pick their children up, much to the astonishment of the panel who berated them for not making the appropriate arrangements as they may need adjourn which would mean three-month delay. Ben lost it then and started to argue that it was ridiculous and so selfish of them both. They couldn't care less and started to emotionally blackmail the panel that their children would be left alone. The twins' team were exasperated. Luckily one of the panel representing the authority had a bloody soul and said they could cover the two leavers parts to get this completed that day. As the two left to pick their bloody kids up the panel broke, stating the 5.30 deadline was finite so we need to crack on and get to the closing arguments. The break was tense as both sides took their positions on different floors.

As they walked back into the room both sides knew this was it, the final chance to convince the panel what they felt was best for the twins. The bean counting authority focused, getting away with as little as possible and using all their skill, knowledge, and guile to convince the panel they could meet he needs of the twins. Two parents and a school that were just doing what they felt right 'to meet the needs of their twins', to give them the very best start in life. A juxtaposition, the panel the arbiters sat on a decision that would change the life of the family.

As the tribunal ends, both have given it there all. The papers and evidence are now with the panel and both sides have fought their corner. As Ben and Lou leave, Ben heads straight for the nearest boozer and sinks a couple of pints with Lou and dissects the day.

They drive home completely exhausted and emotionally and mentally broken ready to pick up the care when they get back. There is no time for tiredness, no break – it's relentless.

Chapter 14

Going Mainstream

They wait nervously for 8 weeks for the panel's decision. The letter arrives on a random Tuesday, Lou is mid caring for the twins who have had their personal care time, meds and dressed ready for the day listing to Moppa Top's Shop. Lou zones out, listening to 90's greatest hits in the kitchen singing along to the Seahorses song Love is the Law. This is Lou's life – a relentless routine, 7 days a week. Her break is doing housework and happily singing at the top of her voice. As the mail drops onto the mat, Lou sees an elasticated bundle including two large A4 brown envelopes. Lou's heart rate drops, and she turns the music off. Snapping off the elastic band reveals an emblem of a Lion, Crown and Unicorn with the words, HM Courts & Tribunals Service. Lou feels the blood drain from her cheeks and sits down at the kitchen table.

Lou texts Ben and he replies – 'ring me'.

'Have you opened it?' Ben asks over the phone.

Lou peels open the letter and starts to read the pages through.

'What does it say?'

'Reading now, it's a large document.'

Lou speed reads through the pages, reading some paragraphs out to Ben, particularly the positively written ones. The document covers the tribunal process and both sides' arguments with comments made by the panel.

'Have we won or not, Lou?' Ben asks, becoming impatient.

'Ben, hang on I am getting to it, I cannot tell at the moment.'

As Lou gets to the end of the document the sentiment in the letter starts to talk about public money and that the authority only having to meet the basic needs and not give a 'gold standard' education. As Lou turns the last page there it is in bold letters; The panel have agreed that Kelston Primary School can meet the needs of Ted and Holly and they can start as agreed on the 3rd of September.

Lou breaks down, heartbroken. A year of preparation, hours and hours of form filling and meetings to get to this. Ben swears and kicks the bin, slamming his fist into the wall.

'I need to go, I cannot fucking believe this,' Lou says.

'Speak to the school to see if we can appeal.'

Lou puts the phone down and calls Sheena who explains that is highly unlikely that any appeal would be successful unless new evidence is unearthed. Lou can tell from her voice that she's upset. She has spoken to Alistair, and they will support but do not recommend that Ben and Lou appeal the decision and look again at secondary stage.

Realising that they have lost, Lou doesn't have the energy to fight anymore and sees the enormity of what she is up against.

Lou goes through the mail. The other envelope is from the local education authority. The letter outlines the next steps should the authority win, which they have – very overconfident. Lou is suspicious. It outlines a meeting with the school and educational representatives, social care, school transport, what they would cover and the start date at the new school. Lou holds off calling them to confirm receipt of the letter while she works out how this would work.

The first day of term was a military operation. Lou started the preparation weeks into August ready for the 'big day'. The school transport arrived – a large ambulance-style vehicle dropped down its hydraulic ramp and Lou wheeled one twin after the other in tears, reeling off instructions to the escort and driver. Lou sent a CD player with the twins to keep them occupied and gave them the biggest kiss. As the van disappeared off down the road, Lou walks back into the house closes the door and walks into the kitchen. She puts her hands on the worktop and her head drops down – it just doesn't feel right. Lou gazes over, heart beating fast. She feels like a wild animal without her cubs. Spotting her car keys, she makes a decisive decision, jumps in the car, and makes her way to school. Lou cannot let go. It is all too much.

Pulling up at the school, she makes her way to reception and ask to see he twins. They are in the reception class, sat at the back with Bianca, their teaching assistant. Bianca is new and has not even met the twins. She's in charge of the twins and two other children with different disabilities. Bianca holds the care plan under her arm, trying to talk to the 'non-speaking' twins with Ted smiling and Holly crying. Lou steps in and calms Holly down and then spend the next three hours helping Bianca and pacifying the twins. The teacher at the front of the class just carries on regardless, ignoring the back of the class interruptions. The youngsters' gaze is constantly dawn to the twins in their chairs. Most of the children had never encountered disability and were not prepared for this. Before Lou leaves, she enquiries about the new toilet and changing area as per the tribunal. One of the school administration staff leads Lou to the area at the back of the school and Bianca explains.

'The children are being changed in here and it will also be used for toilet when their over toilet adapted chairs arrive from the British Red Cross'.

Lou knows without the adapted over toilet chairs the

children cannot use the toilets. They need the strapping and fastenings to keep the children safe and upright.

Lou looks puzzled and enquires about the fact it doesn't look new as agreed in the tribunal.

'Have you not created the new block for the adapted toilet area near the classrooms? The local authority told the tribunal they would have this ready before we started.'

Bianca cannot look Lou in the eye and states 'No, we have decided to use the store cupboard, and this is where the changing table is.

'And where are the toilets going to go?' Lou asks sternly pointing to the adjustable changing tables.

Bianca continues 'we were told to use the old staff toilets at the end of the corridor to put the new adapted toilet chairs over and wheel them down here to change on the changing table beds.'

'This isn't what we agreed, these are not even close to the classrooms.' Lou states despairingly.

'Sorry I don't know anything about this, something about school budgets.' Bianca explains.

'Christ alive, this is terrible, what about their bloody dignity.' Lou shakes her head.

Lou is aware this is not Bianca's fault and makes an apology to Bianca but cannot let this go.

Lou checks on the twins again, speaks to the head and leaves. She's starting to realize that what is argued and agreed in tribunals is not what is delivered, once you leave that court room, you are at the mercy of the authority to deliver what they feel is just enough. As one battle ends another begins. Lou had regular meetings with the school and had to accept that as long as the twins were safe, being educated and happy that was that.

She was often called to collect the twins due to staff shortages usually the night before, or the morning before they even left for school or during the day. As the twins were toileted at school, if there weren't enough hands to get them out of their chairs then they would just be changed again, though two people were needed. If that cover wasn't there, then they would have to come home. Social and Health were completely silent and for all the input fighting the parents, had disappeared into the ether. Lou pressed social care for more funding for extra care, particularly within holidays. The battles were relentlessness and social care used everything in their armoury to avoid, ignore, or refuse any extra funding. The little they gave through direct payments just put all the pressure back on Lou to find her own care. Within the law they were classed as children, the social worker kept saying. It was the parents' responsibility. At least nobody repeated what the first social worker had said losing her temper with the parents; 'well you decided to keep them.' Every time Lou met at the periodic reviews of the twins, the school had all the evidence to say that the twins needs were being met and they were being educated. The gaps in people supporting were just 'one of those things' and 'couldn't be anticipated.' The conversations were circular, and Lou realised that until the twins hit 11 there was nowhere to go. The only way out was if the school said they couldn't meet the needs of the twins.

Chapter 15

The Cats Out of the Bag

They were now two years into primary education and were getting used to the chaos and the school were now starting to creak, being honest with the parents that they were struggling with delivering the curriculum.

Lou used the small number of direct payments she was receiving extremely sparingly and did most of the care herself, full time work was now a distant memory. It made holiday periods problematic as Ben was working full time and Lou was home alone a lot. Megan and Jake would spend most of their holidays away from the family home and when they did have friends round, Lou tried to accommodate but care came first. Lou ploughed on, smiling through it, and smashing a bottle of Cava and a couple of reds down in the little down time she had at the end of the day... every day, with Ben. While he feigned interest, Ben really wasn't into Lou's daily care and authority woes.

Ben had his own issues, mainly financial created by himself. He would disappear off to the desk under the stairs and open the bundle of credit card and loan statements trying to balance the books. When he failed, he would then just put them away in a bankers box, burying them away with the issue.

Ben and Lou then got an invitation to dinner with Aidan and Fran. Fran had been pushing for Lou and Ben to attend. Although Aidan was clumsy and inappropriate with is comments on just about everything and Lou did her best to avoid any contact after the initial kiss. It was summer and Lou reluctantly agreed to Ben's pressure that they should go out and spend time with friends. All the pressure was on Lou to get a night organised, and the twins cared for, for a precious few hours out. Lou rang the agency and booked two carers to be doubly sure the twins were ok.

Ben decided to go out to the cricket all day. This put all the pressure on Lou to run around and get the final care elements in place ready to go. Lou drops Ben a few texts during the day, not to get pissed and remember to be home to change ready to go out. Ben works hard to contain his drinking in the sunshine. When he eventually does come back, slightly worse for wear, Lou gives him a small bollocking as he is later than agreed. Lou has managed to shower the children alone again, give them their meds, change them for bed and get all required for just a few hours out. She shoots off to the shower while Ben cracks open a beer and slumps onto the sofa watching In the Night Garden on TV with the twins. As the carers arrive, Ben lets them in and has a chat in the kitchen. Lou comes down, hurrying things along and starts the handover and shows the new carers the plan she has created. Lou lifts the twins into bed and attaches their feeds, goes through the bedroom equipment with the carers. She settles the children down, puts on their lullabies, fires up the CCTV and closes the door. The carers perch in the lounge to watch the CCTV.

On the journey there, Ben is incredibly bright and bubbly, he has been at the cricket all day with the lads and there is skip in his step. He normally is not so keen on dinner parties anymore.

Fran and Aidan's place is spotless, perfectly pristine in

every way but slightly dated and twee. The dinner party is made up of the usual suspects and Ben and Lou move around the group giving the obligatory kisses on both cheeks. Lou had made a conscious effort not to show any signs of tiredness, went in armed with three topics of conversation and wanted to avoid any and all discussion of the twins, their disability or 'how it was going.'

She managed to dodge and weave all conversations about the twins and focused on Meg and Jake. Biting her lip listening to the usual prejudices that her friends had against disability, the working class or their contempt for people do not like them. Ben rekindled his love of dinner parties and topped up his alcohol consumption. Lou was surprised how overly funny he was being, acting like the court jester. Her sister Hetty was laughing along at everything Ben said, a twinkle in her eye.

Through the dinner party unbeknown to the rest of the guests they were making eyes at each other playing back in their minds the lake district night away and trying desperately at playing cool.

Ben had a notion that he wasn't going home with Lou that night as Hetty had opened up the option of the spare room to allow him a bed and the chance to have some time together when Phil was sleep.

Lou had a hard stop and had to get back to relieve the carers. Ben knew this and absolutely played it to his advantage.

As the night progressed, Lou was mentally knackered listening to the conversations and avoiding what she really wanted to talk about.

Most of the conversations were not really appropriate, Lou had lost the connection with the group and had had enough of the group's lack of thought and empathy. They were openly talking about sensitive issues relevant to Ben and Lou's situation in the disabled world. Ben was less sensitive and almost talked about it as if he wasn't even part of a disabled family.

Lou felt that if they wanted to talk about their prejudices

then do it by all means and share your lack of empathy with each other but, not whilst in their company for God's sake. She smiled and sipped her water, not really involving herself in the conversations so as not to end up screaming at one of her friends. After a few hours, she felt she had stayed long enough and leaves to relieve the carers with Ben suggesting he stays at Hetty and Phil's. Ben and Hetty's plan starts to slot into place.

As the dinner party moves from a conversational one to a kitchen party, Phil calls it and starts the negotiation with Hetty to leave. After an hour of sober negotiation with a pissed Hetty encouraged by Ben, Hetty, Phil and Ben leave together.

Hetty is in the front passenger seat and is turns to talk to Ben in the back. As Phil concentrates on the road ahead, Ben and Hetty make jokes. Ben is sat behind Phil laughing and undoes his flies and gets his knob out, flopping it about at Hetty while he starts talking seriously about work. Hetty is trying not to laugh and replies to Ben's points about office politics. As they pull up to Phil and Hetty's house, Ben does his flies up quickly and he gestures 3.30am to Hetty.

As they get into the house, Hetty shows Ben to his room and then they both come down to the kitchen.

Phil's knackered and says he is going to bed, leaving Ben and Hetty in the kitchen. They may not need to 3.30am 'glass of water' after all.

As they crack open a bottle of Champagne, they chat. They both flirt in their drunken stupor and are touching and pawing at each other. After 45 minutes or so, Hetty pushes Ben away and creeps up the stairs to check in on Phil in bed. He is snoring. She carefully pulls the door closed and creeps back downstairs. She pulls Ben in, and they kiss passionately. Ben lifts Hetty onto the worktop, their hands all over each other. Ben undoes his trousers and boxers, rides Hetty's skirt up around her waist and slowly pulls down her cream thong. Hetty cannot control herself and against her better judgement allows Ben with a push to slowly insert himself into her. He squeezes Hetty's arse cheeks towards him and she moans softly with pleasure.

While they make love in the kitchen, they don't hear the creak of Phil waking up to go to the loo. Phil wanders down the stairs in his boxer shorts and sees the light emitting from the cracks around the kitchen door and hears the music and movement and grunts. Thinking they have both passed out, he pushes open the door to check they are both ok.

Phil's eyes take in Ben, his brother-in-law, trousers round his ankles, pumping his topless wife, skirt round her waist. A few seconds pass by as Phil, fuming, surveys the scene. Ben and Hetty don't stop, they are too pissed to hear over the music. Phil folds his arms and just waits. The longest seconds in Phil's life pass by watching his marriage disappear in front of his very eyes.

Ben is about to climax and going hell for leather, trying to shoot his load. Hetty forces her head back arching her back. 'Don't come inside me, Ben,' she says.

As she does, she catches the open door with Phil, arms folded just waiting for this to stop. Hetty shouts, 'Ben stop!'

'I'm nearly there,' Ben groans.

Hetty pushes Ben away with his hard on still waiting to finish. Ben follows Hetty's gaze to the open door and see's Phil. He startles and pulls up his boxer shorts and trousers, trapping his erect penis in his zipper.

Phil calmly just stands there and then just asks, 'What the fuck are you doing Hetty?'

'Phil, I don't know what to say.'

Ben then chirps in, 'Phil...'

'Ben, shut the fuck up and get out of this house.'

'Ben hasn't got a car,' Hetty says.

'I don't give a fuck, get a cab, leave now Ben before I lose it.'

'Phil...' Hetty pleads.

'No, Hetty, he needs to go now.'

Ben looks at Hetty. 'You going to be ok, Hetty?'

'Yes Ben.'

Ben walks past Phil who just glares and tightens his folded

arms together.

Ben shuffles out. Hetty, now half-dressed, walks past Phil. She catches Ben at the door.

'Ben, my car's open on the road, jump in that, sober up and sleep this off until the morning. You won't get a cab now at this hour. Go now, go!' she says.

*

Phil has turned the music off and is waiting for Hetty in the kitchen, arms leaning back onto the worktop, staring at the spot where his brother-in-law had just finished shagging his wife. He looks across at Hetty who is sheepishly leaning on in the doorway. She's sobered up very quickly.

'How long?' Phil says.

'Only a few months, Phil.'

'Months! He's your brother-in-law.' Phil looks disgusted. 'Have you shagged in our bed?'

'No. No Phil, we haven't!'

'I don't know what to say Hetty. Does Lou know?'

'No.'

'Hetty, do you love him?'

Silence.

'You do, don't you?'

Hetty still doesn't answer.

'I will be in the spare room Hetty – I can't handle this.'

Hetty is in tears and just stands there looking at the scene of the crime. After Phil heads upstairs and slams the door, Hetty makes her way up too and falls on the bed. After just a few hours' sleep Hetty wakes and gets up and goes to the bathroom looking like shit. The enormity of what has happened hits her as she looks in the mirror. Now it's about damage limitation. As Hetty opens the door slowly, she looks across to the spare room and the door is open and the bed made. The whole house is empty, Phil's car keys are gone. Hetty walks into the hall and there is a shadow at the front door

Assuming Phil is back to talk, she smartens herself up and opens the door. It's Ben.

'Phil's gone, Ben.'

'I know, I saw him leave this morning.'

'Did he see you?'

'No.'

'What are we going to do?'

'I don't know. Let's see how this settles down. See if you can get hold of Phil. We need time. I don't want Lou to find out about us from someone other than me. I want us to own the narrative.'

'I will get you back to Lou now. We need to think this through and fast.'

Hetty drops Ben around the corner. He gives her a kiss and lets her know he will text later. He pulls himself together before he opens the front door.

Chapter 16

Moving Out, Moving On

As Ben was leaving with his bags, he looked back at Lou. He was leaving his children, for what? What? What was worth leaving all this behind for – Lou's sister?

When Lou first met Ben, he was one of those boys that all her friends were desperate to catch a date with. Lou first heard of Ben through a friend. This tall, cool, and handsome guy – funny and really sporty. Ben had been through private education. Starting at the local village primary school, he went onto a paid finishing school which was a feeder for the local private high school. At this school Ben met a cohort that shaped him, his friendship group, and his character. Old school rugby boy, rah rah's with an adoring following. Lou often joked with Ben about this. The night Ben and Lou officially met, at a local roller disco, Lou was with the group of friends she had been with, it seemed, forever. From Primary school through to her education at the local grammar school. Lou's group had been so close, and Lou looked up to her friends. They were all beautiful, cool, and very popular. Ben and Lou were the fairy-tale come true.

That first contact made Lou's heart skip a beat, floundering around on their skates. Ben held Lou's hand and gripped it so tight. It was a whirlwind romance and Lou had never felt so happy. Ben and Lou went to the same university, studying different degrees but sharing so many great times. From university they then went onto separate jobs. Ben focused on finance, and Lou went into accountancy, not really using her degree. After marrying, Ben and Lou had an amazing year together partying, socializing, and holidaying. Soon after, Jake came along and then Megan. As a family, they felt bomb proof and wanted an even larger family. Their friends were all having children at the same time. Birthing classes and pre-school friends came in and out of their life.

The twins brought adversity, uncertainty and a new not normal 'normal'. This new world had sent Ben spiralling. A little bit of each of them died that night, never to be re-ignited.

Ben looked back at Lou as he walked away. That beautiful smile and that engaging eye contact had been replaced by a look towards the floor. He turned away and slouched off to his car with just a couple of bags hanging from his arms and drooping shoulders. How had the fairy-tale connection from that first eye contact ended up here? *What changed, what changed – why us?* he thought.

Desperate and final – the situation had beaten them.

Ben only had himself to blame. If he had listened in those early days or knew how it would play out, he could have saved the situation, keeping his dick in his pants.

Ben been cheating on Lou over the years with many others but having an affair with Lou's sister was the final death knell. This had all come from Phil, not Ben or Hetty. Lou had suspected for a while, that her sister and husband were too close and worryingly inappropriate. The odd touch here and dance there should have been the warning signs. Phil had told her how he had caught them red handed in their house. Lou confronted Ben about it. She was willing to work it out together for the sake of the children and their circumstances with care and the burden of the twins. Separate bedrooms and lives but carry on splitting care and the family load. Cash was a real worry with Ben. Although he worked in and understood finance, he was a gambler, spender, and all-round loose cannon when it came to money. He had left not only their situation but also a mountain of debt and a lifetime of worry for Lou.

Ben's mum and dad, Hannah, and Robert, had lost almost everything with his gambling. Betting on red and the ball landing on black again and again. Ben had been betting with other people's money. He was very clever and managed to convince people through a mixture of coercion, stories of greatness and false promises, blending with his charismatic charm. He felt his wealthier mates were fair game and easy prey, he felt entitled to their cash. Even though he was earning good money, he could not offset his loses.

Ben was a clever guy, good conversationalist, funny and falsely trusted by most. He had worked for a large estate agency and climbed his way up the greasy pole. Through the old boy's network, boozy nights out with the right people, Ben had navigated himself into a good position at work and was close to getting the top spot in his area for promotion. However, since the twins' arrival Ben had been side-lined.

Ben had come home furious one evening, reaching straight for a bottle of red wine. Lou remembers the night distinctly – his face and pure fury as he stomped through the door.

'What's wrong, Ben?' she had asked.

'Fucking Barry at work.'

'Ben, the twins are coming down after the day please don't shout.'

'I cannot fucking believe it; you know the job?'

'The promotion to Director?'

'Yes. I had some time with him today to scope out the role.'

'What was said?'

'I asked about the new role as Barry had been ignoring me. We sat down and said I was ready to test myself and press on. Barry then went straight at me about the twins, asking all sorts of questions about outcomes, severity and how we were coping.' Ben took a big gulp of red wine. 'I asked him what that had to do with the job?'

'Ok,' Lou says.

'Well, he said "it's important as my brother has an autistic son, you know? and it's really affected him and the family."'

'What's Autism got to do with this – the twins have Cerebral Palsy, not autism.

'I know, I know, I know.' Ben slugged back the wine and refilled his glass. 'I said I knew this, but we could cope, and the extra money would help us cope and pay for extra care and adaptions. 'He said he understood but the "pressure from the top" you know.'

Lou was shocked.

'So, I cannot be a partner because of my disabled children'.

This floored Ben. He was supposed to be number one choice, pole position before the birth of the twins, and it was a double bubble salary boost which would have alleviated a lot of financial issues. Lou was never made fully aware of the seriousness of the situation and as the daily statements and credit cards landed on the doorstep. Ben was always quick to tuck them away in his office, hiding any evidence.

After realising that he was going to be overlooked, Ben then made some bad choices as he decided to get the salary uplift by other means, and this involved some illegal manoeuvres at work. He knew it was only going to get tougher with the twins, more physical and more fights with the authority. His time for a career had passed. Cash was a constant problem.

At the worst possible time, his mates at work and fellow senior management had worked out that Ben had been siphoning money off to a school pal who was falsely invoicing. Ben got caught red-handed and told to pay back the full amount with interest. He was then asked to gracefully resign and find another job – nothing else would be said. The house was re-mortgaged while he still had 6 months of wage slips to pay the money back in full. They did what they had to do, and Lou thought what a fool she was after standing by him.

Robert and Hannah had also dipped into their pension early to pay off some of the debt. Ben had been gambling and lost the whole lot and then some. This was on top of the credit card and loan debt that he had compiled over the years. Things had been precarious and although some of the debt was known, a lot wasn't. Lou just didn't know where he been spending the money. How many other women were there? Once she knew of Hetty she started to worry there may be more and maybe that had been soaking up the cash.

Phil's disclosure, warts, and all, about the affair with Hetty was heart-breaking. After Hetty was confronted by the extremely mild-mannered Phil about rumours and what he had witnessed – Hetty coughed for the lot. The business trips that weren't, weekends away with her 'best friend' that weren't and the innocent flirting that was definitely not innocent. Phil spilt the lot to Lou, and she was kicking herself thinking what an idiot to not see the signs.

Lou's 24/7 schedule running at 110 miles an hour meant she either missed the signs or ignored them.

*

Ben and Hetty had been complicit, both to blame. Hetty by a mix of lust, sympathy, and sibling rivalry. Had Hetty always wanted Ben and has she been insanely jealous of Lou and Ben from the start? Did their situation make Ben more vulnerable, weak, or just looking for an escape from the day-to-day grind?

What really hurt was that Ben had been caught out more than once with Hetty by Ferg and Rachel. Ferg had a very close alliance with Ben through school and into business. Their dealings together made them thick as thieves. Ben and Hetty had been caught some way away from West Bridgford in a village pub in Woolsthorpe. Ben promised it was innocent, but they were too far away from home for it to be the case. Even worse, was at the dinner party at Toby and Lexi's when Lou had to leave to pick up the night care. Ben had been caught in the act in a downstairs changing room by Rachel – she was mortified but, drink was blame and it was all very innocent. Really! Rachel and Ferg were sworn to secrecy to protect Lou. *WTF? Protect me, for god's sake. How about not doing it in the first place.* Lou thought. As most of the group stayed over that night, what else had happened – who slept where and with who? The one thing she was sure of was that she didn't and wasn't part of any of whatever was going on, too busy caring for their children.

Lou and their twins were where they were because of Ben's financial gambles and lack of integrity. Having almost lost his parents' house, he had gambled theirs away, re-mortgaging and re-mortgaging and creating loans on loan against the property. Not to the value of the property but well beyond. Somehow, and God knows how, during a period of juggling and spinning financial plates they had managed to secure a two-bedroom bungalow on an old people's cul-de-sac on the quiet side of old West Bridgford. A step down from their five-bedroom house on Trevor Road. Once in a prime location, within walking distance from the chic West Bridgford high street, they were now perched on the edge of West Bridgford closer to Clifton than where they wanted to be. The bungalow was shabby tiny and hadn't been changed since 1960. There was no cash to modernise. The only blessing was the size of the living/dining room as this gave them enough space to sleep in the lounge, add changing facilities and be able to watch TV when time allowed. Megan and Jake spent more time sofa surfing at friends and holidays with relatives than at home as there was so little room.

When Ben left, Lou had no choice but to add herself and the twins to the social and council house list as the twins would need their own room one day. Although at the time there were no suitable properties, Lou thought it was the best thing to do. She felt hopeless given the circumstances they found themselves in and that they may eventually lose the bungalow.

Lou had a secret bank account from childhood that she used when needed but this was running low. It did supplement her outgoings and paying bills as they came in.

Ben had basically been paying interest on the loans and cards he had, any living expenses were being covered by Hetty. Phil had moved out and Ben had moved into Hetty's house. A lovely place in the suburbs of West Bridgford. Phil and Hetty had re-mortgaged the house in Hetty's name, Phil had given Hetty the mortgaged house as part of the separation and he took the cash and disappeared. Ben was still juggling everything financially but the biggest worry keeping him awake at night was the missed payments to the Manchester gang. They were overdue and all lines of credit were dry. He had no way of raising the money. Hetty's house was fully mortgaged to pay Phil out so there was no cash there and she wasn't prepared to sell her only asset for a small amount of benefit and hand over to the Manchester scheme, which was running behind schedule and its big pay-day nowhere near happening. It had already swallowed up a lot of cash with another huge investment overdue. Ben had not paid and had no way of paying. Administration and planning delays kept bringing the project to a standstill, but the payments were set and could not be moved – people needed paying. Ben's precarious financial web meant he had nowhere to go and had to let Hetty lead. All financial decisions were now with Hetty and Ben effectively owned nothing, handing his monthly salary straight to her. Ben was now financially off grid.

Chapter 17

A Fresh Start

Lou was hanging onto Jake, just. His moods were getting darker and with the constant gaming, his friendship groups were a mixture of new friends at school, not like his old friends, and a new set of online friends from around the world – the US in particular who were online at night which really worked for Jake. He was pale, skinny, and looked like shit.

Lou couldn't put her finger on where Jake was going in life. He was smoking weed at friends' houses and lived on McDonalds, pizzas, and Coke. Lou was so pre-occupied with the twins that she could feel Jake slipping away but running the entire care regime restricted her time to sort him out. They were like ships passing in the hallway.

It all came to a head when Jake had disappeared off to school, curtains closed tightly, and the door slightly ajar with the blue glow of the laptop seeping into thc hall. Deppy had arrived to assist with care and was looking over the twins for Lou.

Lou decided to go into her son's room for the first time in a long time. It was an absolute shit tip with McDonald's boxes, dirty plates, and cups everywhere. The bed was unmade, dirty clothes were piled high on dirty clothes. The desk in the corner was like a temple to the gaming gods with speakers, controllers, and screens everywhere. Lou walked slowly through the piles of crap; the only pathway was to the desk. Lou flung open the curtains and started to gather the piles of clothes and rubbish. Out of the corner of her eye, she couldn't resist checking the laptop and shut the screen down. As Lou looked back to ensure the coast was clear, she slowly lifted Jake's laptop screen up to turn it off. Her face dropped. On the screen was a website with named women and blindfolded young girls. She scanned the screen, hand covering her mouth in shock. This was extreme porn – sadistic and nasty stuff. Taking a deep breath, she presses back on the browser buttons. As she scanned the saved pages going backwards, she was horrified. Strangulation, gang rape and underage girls and boys being forced into sex.

Lou shut the laptop down and slumped onto the bed. How has it come to this? What do we do next and why? No husband to talk to, Lou had lost touch with most of her old school parent friends with boys of a similar age. This violent porn had entered Jake's life without her noticing. What else was Jake using the internet for? Lou knew the games Jake was playing online were violent but that was a virtual world, not real. The site Lou had viewed were real people with real lives. She couldn't believe that her son would enter this cruel and sexual world.

Jake had changed as a person as soon as the news and reality of his new brother and sister's condition became apparent. In situations where Jake was the only extra pair of hands, his care was cold and resistant and if either of the twins did not do as they should, he soon lost his patience. By now, he was completely absent from all care and would simply not be there when needed. But this discovery was a whole new level. It sent a chill through Lou. This was not the Jake she knew. How had she lost touch with her beautiful boy?

With an absent father, pre-occupied mum and a house

that looked and operated as a care home and a brother and sister that he had no emotional attachment to whatsoever, Jake blamed the twins for everything wrong in his life.

Lou's son, now 15, needed help and direction before he hit adulthood. He was angry, resentful; and had totally withdrawn into the digital cesspit.

Jake was spending time split between Lou's dad and mum who just let him come and go. Increasingly though, he would backpack up and spend more time with friends who were single parent households and let their kids come and go – back in the day, they called them 'latch key kids'. Jake dressed head to toe in black, headphones in listening to metal music to block out the world. Pale, hair all over the place – a world away from the sporty, handsome, pleasantly outgoing young boy.

Ben had no time for Jake 2.0 – he disliked his own son and everything he stood for. He was embarrassed at what Jake had become, the way he looked, and his new friendship group of what Ben called 'saddo's and wierdos'. Jake avoided his dad at all costs.

Once an incredibly popular, 'cute' sporty boy, Jake had seen a string of girlfriends in his younger years. His floppy fringe, funny personality, and sporting prowess was a standout for most girls, and he was loved by all the yummy mummies. Now, Jake hung out with the outsiders, girls who enjoyed the same music, fashion, and gaming scene as him. The majority knew nothing of Jake's home life, especially his disabled brother and sister.

Jake's foray into cruel porn and snuff movies had started to warp his view of life and sex.

After a few days, Lou built up the courage to tackle Jake. It didn't go well. Lou waded straight in, and Jake kicked off, shouting about a lack of trust , leaving Lou in tears and distraught. He swore, smashed up his room and left with a full bag of gaming gear and phone chargers, barging his mum out of the way.

He went to his friend Caleb's, sat down with Sheila, Caleb's mum, who said it was ok for him to stay. Sheila text Lou to say her son was OK and safe. Lou then worked hard to build a communication channel to Jake. It took a while to build back but after a few days Jake would reply with one-word texts. This improved over time, but Jake now had his excuse to be away from the care regime and his dad.

Caleb lived in the Meadows which was an earthy mass council estate not too far from West Bridgford. It was a multicultural area and was known for being rough and gritty. Sheila was a single mother and took Jake under her wing. A hard-working local mum who had a spare room and loved the fact that her only son had found a brother from another mother. Caleb was a secondary boy and Jake was clinging on to his cossetted school education in West Bridgford, now separate from his sister Megan who was still at the private high school funded by Lou's mum and dad. Jake had been asked to leave the high school for dealing blow, Caleb had been expelled from his school for the continual smoking of weed. The last straw has been when he sparked up in his Geography lesson.

Jake was now clinging on at the local high ranking secondary comprehensive school in West Bridgford. Poor attendance and attitude were killing off any chance of coming out with anything resembling grades good enough to go onto further education. The boys would often prize themselves out of their pits, put their uniforms on, leave the house and go off in different directions to their respective schools or go the local McDonalds on Trent Bridge, wait for Sheila to leave, and then go back home to continue gaming, listening to Marduk and spliffing up knowing Sheila wouldn't be back until after 6.30pm.

When Jake thought of home, dark thoughts always came over him. Usually brought on by the incredibly strong super silver haze blow. The thoughts were always for about the twins and all the negative changes they brought into his life. Jake took every opportunity to give Lou the run around knowing she was running at 100 miles an hour day and night. Lou would often frantically call Sheila at all hours of the day and night to check where Jake was and that he was ok. Jake ignored most calls and texts from his mum, but actually enjoyed her checking in on his welfare in a sadistic kind of way.

*

Lou has lost her sister, husband, friends, Jake, and most of her family. She couldn't trust anybody. The only constant through the last few years had been her social worker and closest friend, Terry. Megan is still there for her mum but, is more of a child carer caring for her carer mum.

Megan was second born. As a baby she was placid, and Jake warmed to her but, as she entered the 'terrible twos' the relationship started to fracture and as Megan became more vocal 'with attitude' the more her and Jake fell out. Things started with the odd 'no' then 'the push' then 'the hit'. Tricky times for mum and dad, acting as referees. As Megan left the 'terrible twos' she became even feistier and wouldn't hold back with Jake, Meg was sporty and accelerated academically away from Jake with a streetwise edge. Things could escalate quickly between Megan and Jake; Megan was almost the same size but used her steely glare and guile and if Jake kicked off to win the argument before it ever got physical.

If it did get feisty with Jake winding his sister up, she would have a go back at her brother with spirit of a street fighter. It was obvious that Jake was a little bit afraid of his sister at home but never let on to his or her pals. As Jake and Megan passed ages 5 and 6 both then became really close. They realized they had the same friends and that they were not in competition. They had many laughs together and with Lou and Ben were a really tight family unit and loved each other's company.

Megan loved her times away with her best friends and the families, those spontaneous 'let's drive out and glamp in the peaks or Wells' or a last-minute booking with other families. Sunny days exploring, rounders in the afternoon and BBQ evenings, days seemed to last forever. These perfect days Megan realised they were being isolated from the 'other' world around them. A world where the working and non-working class holidayed and relaxed. This world was not a world the family operated in.

Megan observed almost overnight, after the twins were born the, invites slowly start to dry up. It was just a logistical nightmare for the family and for friends to make the allowances required. Megan and Jake were desperate to relive their favourite holidays but there was always a reason why they couldn't go. And the twins were always at the centre of the reason why not.

Megan did exceptionally well at school and was a high-flyer – soaking up homework, assignments, and a very keen reader. The impact of that night on Jake was enormous, like turning off a sun beam. Megan was much more emotionally mature and sensitive and there were tears and questions, lots of questions. 'What will Ted and Holly be like?

'Will they be able to...?'

'Can we still go on holiday with Suzanne and James?'

'Will they walk...'

'Can they talk like me...'

Basically, all the questions with 'no' answers apart from the obvious... it's not a case of will we holiday with Suzanne and James again it's more a case of would they want to make all of the adjustments to come with us. Highly unlikely!

Megan was deep even from an early age before the twins. Lou and Ben tried to keep the sunbeam shining and block the difficulties they were having as much as they could.

Megan was almost attached to Lou's hip. A very special bond between two very special people. Whereas Jake resented every minute of caring, Megan was there for her mum. In a weird way though – not for her brother and sister but for her mum. She felt her mum's pain from such a young innocent age. Megan tried really, really hard to accept the twins but struggled to weld a bond with the twins. Even Megan felt that her brother and sister were just a constant stream of relentless tasks to be worked through by mum. Megan even read the bible and kept to herself felt that it was *gods will, forced to test them.* Megan was not going to let fate (or as it turns out someone's error on that night) break her. Like a test for life and a life test, a test to strengthen the bond with her mum. Even when she had all but moved out of her mum's house and was living with her grandparents.

Terry had been a constant in the later part of the twins' life. Lou and Terry shared long discussions as Lou tried to navigate social care, health, education, and life in general. They talked about life and the struggles of people like Lou and those less fortunate than her that were bringing up disabled children or were carers with no support and nobody to talk to. Without breaking confidentiality, Terry would talk to Lou about his huge caseload and just how bad services were for people on the edge of society, caring and trying to navigate any support services. Terry knew of the dark forces within the authority who were only focused on budgets, money and depriving his cases of what they really needed. Lou, who had never really thought about politics, was starting to realise just how bad the last 15 years had been with successive governments failing to meet the social needs within society. How health and social care were like warring factions battling each other to dodge the care. It was all about politics and Terry and Lou knew where the gaps were. I It was as much about territory, egos, and people as it was about money. It really opened Lou's eyes to politics and society and how the odds were stacked against people and the sliding scale of who got what. Working and non-working class were basically at the bottom of the scale. Lou found herself in the middle and the upper middle class and wealthy who could buy their way out of it – either through lawyers and barristers or by buying in or employing carers. They had resources, financially and intellectually, so they could fight a lot harder to get support or buy it. It really was a meritocracy and not through need more about the world you were bought into. As she saw the injustices all around her, Lou found herself drifting away from her old friends. Lou did feel lucky though in some way that she had exposure to this 'other' world, the real world, where people were just living day to day to eat or fight for a wheelchair or a lying bed board to keep their child safe at night. Conversations about the latest Mulberry handbag or Monclur gilet were a million miles away from Lou's new, kinder world. Lou never thought she would be discussing social injustice or the latest government policy to reduce care and support for her and others like her but, she was, every day.

Terry had been incredibly helpful to Lou, and she found out that she had known Terry for a lot longer than Lou realised. Terry went to a neighbouring comprehensive in Bingham and knew of Lou, her sister, and friends. They had attended the same haunts and roller discos where she had met Ben. They always joked 'talk about six degrees of separation'. Terry was also aware of Ben and his friends; they were very different and did not mix. Terry and his mates called them the Eton Rifles after the Jam song.

As they got to know each other, Lou felt Terry was one of the most caring people she had ever met and was trying desperately to resist the stronger feelings she was having.

Terry had been adopted as a child and Lou remembered his family; they had many children and were always a gang as they fostered. Lou was never quite sure who was his brother or sister as they were a very transient family. She remembers vividly though that the family was always smiling and having a laugh. A real mixture of characters and personalities made them hugely popular but also a family not to be messed with.

Lou remembered Terry and his kind and welcoming smile, even though their friendship groups never mixed.

There is no doubt that his background, parenting, and family circumstances had shaped Terry and his career. After leaving Toothill, Terry had gone to Sheffield Hallam and got a Health and Social Care degree.

Lou and Terry chatted about university and, over coffee, reminisced about the music, films, and starts of their youth. They both loved *The Lost Boys* and *The Goonies* and would even watch old films together in the early evening whilst the twins went off to sleep. Although the twins did not need lullabies and the cots rocking any more, they could still take 2-3 hours to go off to sleep. As Ted drifted off, Holly would start shouting and wake Ted and then roles would reverse. This could go on for hours, sometimes allowing Terry and Lou to watch an entire film whilst keeping an eye on the CCTV and going in to pacify the twins.

Terry tried to make Lou and the family feel like anything was possible with the twins. When Terry was talking to Ben and Lou in the early days, he did explain to the family that they could still be a family but said they would have to adapt and change as the twins grow and develop. He knew what was coming but couldn't give it warts and all!

The many social care meetings when Ben switched off if it wasn't going his way, fiddled with his phone or made a 'work call' which was a diversion rather than facing into the issue. Ben lost his temper a lot with Terry if he wasn't getting his way. He would fire off emails that were mildly threatening, stating he would take legal action. Both knowing they didn't have the money to pay for any legal support. Terry just took it and would build back all of the bridges that Ben had smashed down. Ben thought social care was ridiculous, everybody that worked it was ridiculous and the whole system a farce. For Terry, it was his every day, and his passion was to always do the right thing.

Terry had a huge caseload with 50 children, covering most of the city. Lou and Ben were by far the most complex. Help with direct payment applications and various other form filling really helped when Lou just couldn't cope with anymore and Ben was AWOL. Terry was more than a social worker and a family friend to Lou. They laughed together at the silliest things which really helped with the dark conversations they had to have about the twins. Talking about the twins' futures navigating adult care would be ten times more challenging compared to children's social care and Terry would carefully prepare Lou ahead of time.

One day, when Lou was out shopping with the twins, she saw Terry out with his friends. She remembers thinking his friends just looked normal and were always very friendly to her and the twins. Terry would not have shared that much about their situation but would always make such a fuss with them. Terry would talk about his friends who were either carers, healthcare workers, fellow social workers, or lawyers. All were wholesome human beings and Lou would chat with them regularly if they were out and about and would miss it if their paths didn't cross.

Some of the state-funded equipment needed for the twins' condition was hideous. It would often break or fall apart, and Lou was constantly onto Wheelchair Services which was in Mansfield so quite a trek for her and the twins to get to. Wheelchair Services, like every other service, was hamstrung by cash and they were not allowed to be use the equipment manufacturers they wanted to. They had to use the NHS preferred list, so the child had to fit the equipment, not the other way round.

The local health authority was particularly difficult, and their default position is that would not fund a thing. They put Lou through various tools and tick box exercises to get the very basic health funding they needed. It was like dealing with the mafia and Terry was her law enforcement, he understood the terminology and the rabbit holes health would send service users (as they were called) down, hoping that if it was made hard enough the users would give up, shut up and buy it themselves so the authorities could show a saving. It was incredibly difficult for all 'users' on top of the day to day struggles they have to contend with.

Terry was such a great support. Lou and Terry would talk about the chronic underfunding, over stretched services, and over worked all social care. Health seemed to have a head count of 5-1 when it came to any conversations about funding. Lou would read stories of hospitals full of social care cases blocking beds as there was no service, placement or carers to transition the poor souls back into their homes. She had the constant nagging feeling that she would one day not be there for the twins, then what? Ben didn't want the responsibility.

When Ben left Lou and the situation about Hetty came out, Terry was just about the only person left in Lou's life. She could talk to him about the twins, her feelings and work out a pathway for a future alone with two disabled young adults, one absent parent, one very disengaged young teenager and a withdrawing young teenager. When Lou felt alone, Terry was her rock. They hugged and kissed on the cheek, but Terry knew that that was it, it couldn't cross the threshold. He never stayed over and would always go home after their movie nights. Lou would drink when they were together and Terry wouldn't, he wasn't tee total but knew that this was extended service for who he a lot of feelings for and knew Lou was just about alone in the world. Terry could see Lou slipping into one too many drinks and, along with her prescription drugs, often left Lou either nodding off into a bottle on the sofa or she would stagger off to bed. Quite remarkable as Lou would then turn on the bedroom monitors to complete her 24-hour shift with one ear and one eye open for the entire night before it all started again. And it did all start again with the 6am wake up. Every night was a wine night and Terry didn't want to judge but would often check in with Lou and see if she wanted to talk about it. She never did. It had become a problem but at the end of another day of care this was Lou's out – a little time slipping into the sofa and relaxing into a bottle of wine. Her passing out in the evening became so frequent that she gave Terry a key to the house, just so he could lock up after himself when he left her. Microwaved soup in a mug, cheese sandwich and a bag of cheese tasters was Lou's staple diet. Quick, easy and could be had on her knee switching between the TV and the CCTV with the twins on full volume, listening to every breath, twitch, and movement. The CCTV was a constant and seamless stream between the sofa and the bedroom. When Terry disappeared, Lou would often switch off the TV and nod off on the sofa as she couldn't be bothered to go back the bedroom and an empty bed, knowing it would all start again the next day. There was sporadic direct payment funded care which covered three mornings a week to give Lou assistance. One 'golden hour' of care to help with the personal care for the twins. This was brief moment where Lou could zone out, jump in the shower, and have a coffee in the garden. A moment to breath. The carers, though, were non-clinical so could only do the very basics for Holly and Ted. Assessments of their care and, for the safety of the carers, all moving and handling came with its own assessment and all moving was now hoisted with a minimum of two carers which took most of the hour. Deppy, who was the one consistent carer, was joined on shift by a procession of carers that would come and go. Deppy would often train the new carers on shift as carers would arrive for their hourly slot, one of 12 different placements in one day, not knowing the twins' names or exactly what they needed to do. Deppy was a beautiful person who had dedicated her life to caring in the UK and was a god send to Lou and the twins. They would always get the very best of care when Deppy was on shift. Lou dreaded the times when Deppy wasn't on shift. The agency was only interested in number of visits ticked off, giving the carers very little time from one visit to another, some working 7 days a week. Lou knew that if Deppy was not 'leading' then the carers would not have a clue what they were doing, and Lou became the third carer on shift. The agency just left the carers to their own devices, and they were very rarely supervised.

Terry was Lou's sounding block, and he did all he could to help and advice but did joke that he couldn't fix the care system but would have a bloody good go.

Chapter 18
Guardian Angels

The news was just such a worry. A virus spreading across the world that could hit the twins badly and prove fatal. The chest infection medication may not stop this one. As news of the virus spreads around the world, cases are located in the UK and then it hits Lou that this is really happening. Although it's a worry, the years of caring have taken their toll and Lou has to balance survival for her and the twins and the risk of catching a virus that isn't even local yet.

The twins are now at special school that has clubs after school, transport and, most importantly, they understand how to educate and care for the twins. The twins love it, and it is such a shift from the primary school disaster years. Schooling had taken a sharp turn after a change meeting with a very special lady. Lou had been in Birds café with the twins while Jake was at cricket coaching at Trent Bridge. It was the school holidays and Lou had found a quiet table in the corner and settled the twins in. As Lou was about to get her coffee, she turned around to a lady in her 60's smiling at her.

'Do you want me to watch the lovelies while you get

yourself something?'

'Oh god, that's really kind thank you!'

'What are their names?'

'Ted and Holly.'

'Beautiful. Take your time love, they will be fine.'

'Do you want anything?'

'No, I am fine, thanking you.'

While grabbing a coffee and an elephant's foot cream bun, she takes a look back and the lovely lady is talking to the twins.

'Were they ok?' she says, returning to the table.

'Yes, they were fine.'

'Do you have children?'

'I did. I had a boy called Darren he had cerebral palsy.'

'Did?' Lou asks.

'Yes, he died.'

'Oh no, that's terrible. I'm sorry.'

'No, it's not, he had a full life for the years he was alive and was such a joy.'

Lou doesn't know where to look as she slurps her coffee nervously. 'Sorry I didn't catch your name,'

'My name is Laurna.'

'Hi, Laurna, my name is Lou. Do you mind me asking what happened to Darren?'

'He died of a severe chest infection; I couldn't save him.'

'That's not great.'

'He had already been hospitalised nine times and survived, the tenth one took him. Darren had a full life and we battled together against the odds.'

'God, I know how that feels with these two.'

'Education, Social services, or Health?' Laurna asks, knowingly.

'Education.'

'Where are they now?'

'Primary school in West Bridgford.'

'Did you fight?'

'Yes, we did but lost.'

'Did they fight for mainstream?'

'Yes.'

'Sounds about right, saving money?'

'Yes, definitely it's been a nightmare!'

'Have you made notes?'

'Notes?'

'I was sat where you are now and met a very chatty lady sat waiting for an appointment with her own daughter with Cerebral Palsy at a clinic for Darren's vision when Darren was very young and the best advice, she gave me was to journal everything, every incident, every missed school day, every conversation – everything.' Laurna says. 'And I did. I journaled everything, and I mean EVERYTHING!

When it came to the meetings to discuss educational progress and care I had every incident, every missed educational day and the schools struggles and strains trying to accommodate Darren.'

'Right.' Lou is hanging onto Laurna' every word.

'At every meeting I fed back the year. The school were horrified, and it would have really affected their status which had always been outstanding. In the end we fought together and in the end the school actually fought on Darren's behalf to say they couldn't meet the needs. Darren was moved into a secondary specialist school and college. In the end my journals meant there was no need to fight. My advice, start journaling today, gather all of the information you can, everything. At every review, play back your journal, write everything down and put everything in writing to ensure your babies get everything you want for them.'

As Laurna chatted for a few minutes longer she said she had to go and get the bus.

Lou went back to the café many times but never saw Laurna again to thank her for invaluable guidance and advice.

As Lou entered the last few years of the twins' primary education, she had a significant body of evidence that was shared periodically at the many meetings they had with the school. The school then started to side with Lou who was on a crusade with her journals. The evidence became overwhelming and, just as Lou's guardian angel had indicated, the school buckled. Between them they took on the local education authority together stating that they couldn't meet the twins' needs. The school, not Lou, ended up driving the decision to move schools and Lou could sit back with her journals and watch it play out. The journals were full of missed school days, lack of staff to educate or change the twins and the overall strain it was putting on the school and the other pupils. The local education authority ended up agreeing to the move and the twins were moved to the local specialist school who catered for a range of disabilities and challenges. The staff and the facility were brilliant; fully tracked changing areas, hydro and physiotherapy on site and trained staff. Lou knew the kids were in safe hands and this was a real change. It gave Lou a breather during term time to clean the house and keep on top of the paperwork. Holiday times were tough as it was back to full-time care and Ben would just work through. With the special school though came a caveat from social care – they wanted to reduce their hours. While in mainstream school, Lou had managed to get every morning covered by the agency for personal care and after school, ready for bed care. They wanted to reduce the hours because of clubs and the cost of specialist education – The Local Education and Social Care (the authority) basically gave with one hand and took with the other. Lou managed to negotiate some care, but it was well short of what was needed.

The specialist school was a pathway into college, so it gave the twins a real future. The twins were getting bigger and the strain on Lou had been showing, she was aging quickly and her body creaking under the strains of caring.

There was nervousness at the school as they protected the children who were extremely vulnerable. The twins were mid risk as they were on the whole healthy and had no chest infections. The news got bleaker and bleaker and the transport they were using to get them to school were taking no chances and staff were masked with goggles and disposable gloves. Lou had to put the children on the transport and the school took them off.

As Lou loaded the children and their baggage for another day at school, she waved them off, turned on the radio and listened to the news. It was bleak and lockdowns were just around the corner. As Lou sits at the table with her brew the phone rings.

Lou knows a phone call on the house phone in the day is never good.

'Hi,' Lou picks up.

'Hi, is that Holly and Ted's mum? We are calling all the parents about the current situation. We think we are going to having to shut the school down.' Lou's head drops into her hands. 'What does that mean for the twins?'

'Unfortunately, they will have to be at home until further notice.'

'What! How will that work, who will help me while they are at home?'

'We are unsure at the moment. It's an unprecedented situation.'

'Have you been in touch with social care to see how this will work? Will they support me?' Lou asks.

'Sorry we are unable to help with this at the moment and unsure how it will work, we just wanted to let you know.'

'When will this happen?'

'We think in a couple of days.'

'Days! Days! are you kidding me? This is going a nightmare – for how long?'

'We don't know yet; the situation is moving fast.'

'Fast. Bringing the children home for an indefinite period is simply not going to work, how will I cope?'

I' am really sorry to have to pass on this information, but the children are all vulnerable and we cannot take any chances, all of the children are being sent home.'

'I get that but, this leaves me with no support and no one to help.'

'Yes, I totally understand, and we really are very, very sorry!'

'Ok, so how will I find out when you officially need to close down?'

'Be prepared for it being very last minute. It's likely to be on the day. We will of course let you know.'

God this is all I need, Lou thinks. The twins coming home indefinitely is going to break Lou with her hourly carers all looking to go back home round the world to their families before a global lockdown. Lou's family are all in a disparate state. They're either not around or resilient enough to be there for Lou as she needs them to be. She is not going to start begging them for help now. They just haven't been there to date, so why now? There will be one excuse after another like there always is. A virus and lockdown are the perfect excuse not to help.

In an act of desperation, Lou calls social services to see what plans they have in place – it is constantly engaged. Lou is now desperately anxious.

Left with no alternative, she needs to send an email to social services immediately, she needs answers today. Lou writes out the email asking all the right questions. As she presses send, she just hopes that the authority has made an emergency plan where much-needed care will offer parents some support.

Lou gets an out of office from her current social worker and hears nothing back from the main number, which is nothing more than she expected. It's like doomsday approaching. She leaves a voicemail for Terry to see if he can give her an update. Terry has been promoted to manager and although over sees the twins' case is not the direct contact.

Lou then gets a call from school transport – they are suspending their service, and the twins will need to be collected.

Lou drives through the deserted streets to pick the twins up.

'Oh, shit what's going on?' she mutters to herself as she

approached the school's car park.

Parents are ladened down with bags and equipment, masked up walking frantically back and forward to their cars. There are a few minibuses providing transport for those without any access to cars, vans are being packed up with wheelchairs, equipment, supplies and the kids. Lou's heart sinks.

All of the staff are masked, gloved, and visored up.

'Hi, are you Ted and Holly's mum? We have to give you this letter. Please can you read it?' one of the school secretaries says as she arrives inside.

'What's it about? I haven't got time to read it.'

'The school has had instructions from the government via the authority to shut down until further notice in these unprecedented circumstances. All of the kids' stuff has been packed up and it's in the sports hall ready for you to collect. The twins are in their classroom ready.'

The staff ask Lou to put on all of the protective wear including a plastic apron. As she loads the mountain of items for the twins, the reality of what's happening hits her right in the chest.

After the luggage move, she makes her way down to the twins' classroom dressed like a surgeon. She walks into the room and the twins are completely oblivious. Lou's thinking, *here we go same shit different day for them and me! Indefinitely!*

As she drives home, Lou thinks about the next move, feeling increasingly frustrated. She is going to contact her local MP and he is going to get it warts and all, exactly what she thinks of social services emergency planning and lack of contact.

Lou needs help, she wants to know what's happening and with no contact is feeling completely helpless and doesn't feel she can cope.

Things are ridiculously tight money wise, and carers are scarce, and Lou needs some financial support to get through this. Ben is AWOL and would only add to the stress. Besides, the thought of being locked down with Ben send chills through Lou – she would rather do this solo with agency help. Non emotional help, just functional and structured.

Terry texts Lou to check in and lets her know social services are in turmoil, have no plan and are awaiting central government advise. Terry states that the local agencies and the local authority are going to lose 75% of their carers, some going home to their families before national lockdown kicks in. The whole world is panicking and that doesn't help Lou.

The twins need consistency and after so many chest infections and hospitalisations this is scary enough. They have no interest in the virus, its effect on care or the country – they need 24/7 care – end of story.

Lou has been getting direct payments for the care but there are so many gaps, and it only covers a fraction of the need. Now there is no school time to give Lou a break.

It means Lou will be covering almost all of the care for both locked inside their tiny house. Carers allowance is pitiful, and Ben has been a complete shit giving no time to the twins or to Lou. She has accepted this, but his selfishness is making her extremely bitter, knowing he is shacked up with her sister and does nothing.

Then, ping! Lou gets a reply back from the MPs office. It's not from the MP, it's from a member of his staff. The clown has copied in senior staff at social services with her warts and all request for help. This could go either way. Being the local MP and a minister at that, though, should kick in a positive response.

As the email pings back from social services, they fire back to minister a bland, none-committal 'were all struggling with this 'unprecedented' situation'. Lou reads it thinking to herself, *if someone says 'unprecedented' again I will fucking cry. Come and spend a day, night, weekday, or weekend with me - every day is unprecedented!!*

Lou replies asking for a phone call or email with a plan as soon as possible.

As Lou settles in for the first of many nights and days caring alone while she waits for a call back from social services, the news on TV just gets worse and worse as the virus moves closer to where they live. The world is shutting down.

Lou starts lockdown with gusto, going through the daily routines, sticking today and night times as per the care plans, she created. As the days pass, the situation externally is moving fast. Internally it's slowing down to a snail's pace and the days seem to last for weeks. The twins are aware things have changed and want to go back to school. They are unhappy and Lou is now mother, carer, teacher, nurse, secretary, personal care assistant, playworker. As the crescendo of moaning and shouting from the twins continues, aimed at Lou, she has to have a moment in the garden and let them shout and cry it out. She needs to protect her sanity. After one friend had dismissed Lou's warts and all message about the twins and her new caring regime with a 'same here, we just have to get through this Hun!' Texts from family and her small circle of friends 'checking in' now get the same response. Lou had bitten her lip and hoped her swimming pool wasn't to cool, enjoying her fucking peloton in her home gym and then unpacking the £800 Ocado shop.

Lou is now just replying with one liners.

Breaks from the multi-tasking role she had thrust herself into consisted of wandering around the garden looking up at the sky empty of planes, no traffic passing by the house. This new insular world was like a magnifying glass on her loneliness. She missed things she hadn't had in years. She was missing her family, missing having a partner to share the load, missing having normal conversations with her children. Talking to Jake about his latest sporting achievement, singing to Katy Perry with Megan, laughing, chatting, serving dinner, and sitting at the dinner table. The simple family things that ended so soon after the twins had been born.

As the weeks progress, Lou is struggles to keep up the daily routine for Ted and Holly and the day and night plan starts to slip. Lou gets a call from the agency – Deppy is staying and is coming out of quarantined to assist Lou. Lou is so relieved she could cry.

The 5am shift starts, and Lou goes in to see the twins. Ted is smiling but Holly is not and is grumpy from the minute she wakes. This is going to be a challenging day with Holly as when it starts like this it will end like this. Lou feels that the children are starting to sense the pressure she is under and the uncertainly of the world. As Lou starts to dress Holly on the changing table, the doorbell goes.

Lou is laughing and crying at the same time and punches the air 'yes!', kisses Holly and lets her know Deppy is here. Her crying changes to a frown. Ted is smiling in his chair. As she opens the door, Lou wants to kiss Deppy but can't be due to the visor, gloves, mask, and apron. But does go in for a hug. Deppy is tearful, greeting her with such love it is heart-warming for Lou and a real-life saver.

Deppy hits the ground running, assisting with toileting and personal care. It's been weeks since Lou had this. Holly is safely on the toilet and Deppy tells Lou to go and get a coffee. Lou just walks to the kitchen, floating as this is such a massive relief.

After a short break, Lou and Deppy hoist Holly off the toilet and manoeuvre Ted so he can watch his favourite, CBeebies.

Another email pings in, and reading it very carefully, Lou cannot work out what it actually says.

As she is reading the phone rings – the caller is someone she hasn't spoken to before – Terry's boss, Emma. 'Hi, my name is Emma, and I am Head of Social Services and Homecare for Nottinghamshire City,' she introduces herself. 'I have seen your email and replied back to you.'

'Yes, I have seen it but not read it all. To be honest, I don't understand what it's saying,' Lou says.

'You state in the email that you would like to direct some of your payments to yourself as you are struggling – is that correct?'

'Yes, as I am now providing the majority of care due to lack of carers and have been caring alone,' Lou states.

'You know that the rules mean that you cannot do this?'

'Yes, but everyone keeps saying these are 'unprecedented times'. I cannot work, we are struggling financially and need money. The carers are not providing the care hours we agreed, and I am having to do most of it myself, I have a surplus in the direct payments account, I am asking for some of this to eat and keep the heating on.'

'Yes, I understand these are unprecedented times, but if you do pay yourself, it would be seen as fraud by the authority.'

'Fraud?! But I am doing the care, there are no family members with me. What if I ask a family member to help, can they be paid?'

'No, that would also be fraud. It needs to not be a family member.'

'Like whom? We are in a lockdown? That's ridiculous and you are going to maintain that through this situation, no change or shift in your position. No plan? We are in a lockdown. How will I and others like me cope?'

'I am really sorry, there has been no alternative guidance. That's the position the local authority has taken.'

'So, we will have no carers or access to funds sat in the direct payments account to pay for the non-existent care. I still have to pay the bills and eat – I only want to use this to survive, not using it for luxuries and holidays for God sake.'

'Really sorry but that's our position - have you been taking any of the direct payments for yourself?'

'Are you really asking me that?'

'Just doing my job. If you have then the payments will have to stop to the account.'

'Seriously! You are outright accusing me of theft.'

'I am not accusing you, just asking the question. We will need you to send the statements to be audited.'

'Well, it's not a question is it; you have given me no

solutions – that is pitiful. Sorry but I cannot believe you are hanging us out to dry in a lockdown and its business as usual while you're all sat being paid working from home.'

Sorry, that's just how it is. Please don't raise your voice – these are 'unprecedented times'. If it changes, we will let you know but you cannot pay yourself or family members for care.' Lou holds the phone away and put her hand over the receiver – *fuck you. Unprecedented. You fucking idiot.* Lou can then feel herself tearing up – boiling over. 'Please can you put what you have said to me today in writing please by email?'

'I am not sure why you need that?'

'Because you are leaving me with no solutions, no financial help. How can you live with yourself?'

'We are doing everything we can, I assure you, and will be in touch if anything changes. Please ensure you don't take any money out of the account, or the payments will be stopped, and you will have to reapply.'

'Thank you for nothing!'

Lou puts the phone down incredulous that this is where they are. What a shit show. She is overcome with helplessness again and the anxiety is overwhelming. How many times has this happened over the years?

Deppy is calling for Lou for help with Holly. Ted is also shouting as he hates Pingu and wants the channel changing.

Together they hoist Holly off the toilet and onto the changing table and take care of the customary personal care. Holly won't lay still and smacks Deppy in the eye. The athetosis is strong today with her mood, muscle tone is really high, probably sensing the tension in the house and in Lou. Deppy is taken aback needs some time out, it has hurt her, catching her out. The flailing arm has hit the visor, pulled it down and knocked her glasses off. Deppy needs a little time to compose herself and goes into the lounge.

As Deppy walks in Ted, is shouting over the replacement CBeebies programme and Holly is laughing and squealing inappropriately as she knows she has hurt Deppy after physically lashing out. Deppy composes herself and helps Lou hoist Holly into her chair. As Deppy moves the body sling around Holly, she is mindful of the flailing arms and squalling Holly who is desperate for a repeat of the physical altercation. Lou holds both of Holly's tense arms which are desperately fighting against Lou's grip. Holly starts to spit, and her face is red with the battle. They winch up the hoist and drop Holly into her buggy. As they hold her arms, the push down Holly's hips, wrestling with the waist and shoulder straps to make Holly safe. It's now a war of attrition and Lou and Deppy know there can only be one winner or its game over. As Lou counts out loud to Holly, something she has done to calm Holly and Ted down since they were two, Holly's body starts to un-tense and is safely strapped in.

Deppy then looks at her watch. Her 30-minute appointment is done, and she is overtime. Deppy has to go to another appointment, leaving mum with Ted to sort alone. Ted needs a change but that will have to wait until Lou has both twins calm. Lou knows the risk of hoisting alone and the transfer from chair to changing table to toilet is precarious at best, even with two carers it's problematic as three is the number the occupational therapist has recommended.

Lou puts the twins back in front of the TV and walks into the kitchen, she passes a mirror in the hall and has a brief moment to look at herself. As she stares hard into the mirror, she thinks, *how has it come to this?! I am on my own, knackered, no money, stressed out, look like a sack of shit and we are in a once in a generation pandemic, accused of fraud for trying to survive – how will I cope and how has my life come to this.* Time for a sip of tea before the next shift.

Jake sends a message on the family WhatsApp group; school are talking about locking down and shutting the school and he's going to stay with his mate if it does. Lou knows there is not a lot she can say as Jake is now a distant visitor. Meg sends a message saying the same and she has arranged to stay with Lou's mum and dad and sends kisses to her mum.

This is a lonely road for Lou to tread alone. She understands that it is for the best as she has no capacity or care for anybody else at the moment.

It's all about survival.

Chapter 19

The Clocks Just Stop

The quicksand is softening, Lou is sinking fast. Megan is locked down with her grandparents. Jake is absent, locked down with his mate's mum. Lou's parents are extremely concerned about Lou's health but are sticking to the Covid rules. Since the move to the smaller two-bedroom bungalow, there just isn't enough room for all of family and the endless equipment and paraphernalia needed to provide care for the twins.

The twins' life is now 5 feet apart in the lounge and 3 feet apart in the bedroom. The lounge is the only area for them to be out of bed in front of the TV and if Lou is feeling strong, brief periods on the rug, but still listening to music or watching TV.

The mobile hoist is a bloody nightmare for Lou, clunky and just not built for moving round on rugs and carpets. Carers are still dropping in and out and the latest one turned up and couldn't do anything as the care plan hadn't been provided for her. Lou had lost her temper, not with the carer but the whole bloody situation, the authority, government, society, and the agency's lack of co-ordination. This resulted in either carers that didn't know what they were doing, meaning Lou had to train them and care herself, or carers that just didn't turn up.

It felt like the walls were closing in around Lou and her body was starting to creak. The lack of sleep was getting harder to deal with as the twins were intermittently awake and the constant anxiety that this will never end, or the twins will die because of it.

Lou has been prescribed sleeping pills but cannot take them as needs to have one eye and both ears open constantly. They talk about mothers' instinct, but Lou has had so bloody long of this she has had to cope with 3-4 hours broken sleep for many years. It's beyond bearable. With nothing else to do in the evenings, Lou's drinking has accelerated, just to take the edge off the days and deal with the situation. It started with an extra glass, then an extra bottle then a large Vodka with pain killers. Hangovers have gone as the drinking accelerated and Lou's body just got used to the alcohol and less and less food. She was making mistakes with medication for the twins, but it went unseen as Lou was alone. She would add Post It notes around the house to remind herself to try and reduce the mistakes, but she was falling asleep though in the day. Falling asleep to the Teletubbies or waking up to the Rug Rats.

TV was the daytime babysitter and Lou knew that should be doing more to stimulate the twins. They needed physio, speech and language therapy, hydrotherapy and so much more stimulation, but Lou was running on batteries, and it is just about the basics. Survival. Lou has brief moments now and then to have a brew but tries not to look in the mirror. When she did catch a glimpse of herself in the mirror, she saw looking back at her was not what she expected. She had lost weight; her skin was pale and greasy and had broken out into spots like a teenager going through puberty. Her oversized t-shirt was covered in the twins' spit, formula milk and red Epilim medication. As she raised up the t-shirt, it smelt of sweat and chip fat... Her saggy tracksuit bottoms splattered with her hardened food, red wine spillages draping over her Crocs which looked like they had been used in a sweaty kitchen in Soho. She knows she looks a complete state. But there was nobody else to notice so she didn't give a shit. This was a 5-day outfit, day, and night.

Lou cannot afford to buy new clothes, and nobody ever saw her apart from the other carers or delivery drivers so why bother?

As the twins have their mid-morning nap, Lou goes into the kitchen to listen to the endless news reel of current Armageddon.

'There's worse to come.'

There is no end in sight and cases of the virus are up by 300%. Death rates are up and will continue to rise.

There are now cases all over Nottinghamshire.

Hospitals are at breaking point.

Lou leans back against the worktop. She is so tired and every time she turns on the radio or the TV she starts to cry – she knows why but doesn't know why. It doesn't help.

Lou has lost all sense of emotional control and just wants it all to stop. Dark, irrational thoughts creep in. The alcohol doesn't help and adding a glass of white wine with her lunch break is not helpful either. She starts questioning if life's worth living for her and the twins if this is it. Is it all worth it?

Lou texts Ben to see if he can transfer some money over as she needs to order shopping to be delivered as she cannot go out and leave the twins with another new carer. It's just so complicated.

Lou has been locked down now for four weeks and her only connection with the outside world is the small back garden. It's tiny, overgrown, scruffy, and oppressive. Getting the wheelchairs over the steps and over the uneven scrappy grey patio takes an age. When the twins do get out there, they last for minutes and then the shouting starts, and Lou starts the process of getting them back in. It feels like a complete waste of time.

When the sun beats down, it's red hot and even with the

windows open it's still stifling and all she can smell is bleach, dirty nappies and sweat.

The single toilet that they are all using just isn't fit for purpose and Lou longs for the days of overnight hotel stays back when they had money in their pockets. Comfy hotel beds, ensuite rooms with showers and bathes and no twins. God, a bath. What Lou would do for that now with a glass of wine, candles and Sade playing in the background. All they could afford was ripping out the bath for a walk-in disabled shower.

The bathroom isn't big enough for a family, never mind appropriate for the twins' needs. The shower chair is the bane of her life; it's enormous and transferring using the mobile hoist is problematic. Ted and Megan's athetosis just makes it almost impossible for one person to manage the transfer. Lou relies on the methods she has learned over years, counting to 10 and putting the right song on, which is almost impossible to get right first time, as the song choice changes by the minute.

This particular Monday was not a Manic Monday, it was a nightmare Monday. After a long night, Lou starts the daily shower routine. Nappy rash is a constant issue and cleaning and applying cream is required six to eight times a day for both.

Lou would love to go two days without the shower routine but, the twins being doubly incontinent, it is really needed as the risk of infection is high.

Monday was bad. The dining room is now a personal care, hospital, and entertainment room. Lou hoists Ted out of his chair into the dining room and wheels the mobile hoist, juggling to transfer Ted into his water-resistant sling and keeping an eye on Holly in the lounge who is shouting at the 'TV babysitter'. Ted is having a bad day, and he is angry, in pain and muscle tightness is causing him to be extremely strong. Ted is thrashing about, hitting out. Lou is like a shadow boxer avoiding the flailing fists. Lou manoeuvres the chair into its spot diagonally across the corner of the room and the mobile hoist into position. The hoist looks more like equipment that you would take a car engine out with rather than transfer an adult with. Loaned to the family, you don't have a choice on size, style, and colour – when it's on loan for free you get what you get and just have to get on with it.

The lunchtime carer hasn't shown up, meaning Lou must do what should be a three-person sling transfer alone.

Lou manages to get Ted out of his chair and onto the changing mat on the dining room table, Ted is thrashing and shouting so Lou starts the process of calming him down. He is angry and in pain and cannot straighten his legs out, his legs are tight, and his knee contractures are causing him pain.

Lou does what she can to pacify Ted, she feels for Ted as there is no respite for his spasms, she must ensure she gets him out safely and does what she can do to protect herself. Years of lifting, moving, and handling the twins have left her in a lot of pain herself and although the Codeine and Co-Codamol help her wrists and knees, it still leaves her weak. Teds now out of his chair on the table, thank God the mat has sides! Ted is thrashing and she gets him undressed and changes his pad which is soiled, and his bottom needs a good clean before he gets in his waterproof sling for a shower.

She manages to get the day sling out from under Ted and throws it on the floor. But she can't save it – it's badly soiled. More washing and expense and she will now have to use the crappy back up sling.

As she manoeuvres Ted, he is rolling round, soiled, trying to pull on his gastrostomy tube and smacks Lou in the eye. It hurts and Lou reels back, holding her eye. Ted belly laughs and Lou is fucking furious inside but holds it in as the more she shouts and gets angry at the 'situation', the more Ted will laugh.

Lou crouches down out of sight, head in her hands – her eye is absolutely throbbing. She shuffles over to grab a cold flannel and holds it over her eye with one hand and then holds Ted's torso with the other to try and stop him sliding further down the table. Ted is still thrashing, laughing, squealing and hitting out even though he can see Lou is in pain. Lou breathes deeply and throws the flannel across the room, finding an extra spur of energy. Like an energy drink spurt of power, she slides the shower sling under Ted and wrestles with him, while Ted pulls and pushes against her with all his strength. Lou is not going to lose this battle and holds his wayward arm away from her face, completing the slide positioning and pulling the sling up and around Ted's body.

Weary but fired up by her smack in the eye, Lou secures Ted in the sling, pulls up the sling loops and drags the hoist over. Looping the sling loops, she gets Ted into position and takes a breather. She wheels the hoist and Ted from the dining room. Holly is still shouting at Lou for attention, but Lou is flying solo so Holly will have to wait. As Lou attempts to control Ted's stiff flailing fists, she manoeuvres the hoist over the raised door thresholds, scraping the walls. Lou pushes Ted through into the bathroom, the tiled floor is helpful but incredibly slippery. She pushes the shouting, smiling Ted and hoist towards the shower chair positioned over the toilet. Ted is fully aware that this is his moment, and he will have the upper hand over Lou as the transfer to the shower chair with its securing waist and shoulder straps is hazardous one. Ted knows there is a moment where he is unrestrained and uses the opportunity to take Lou on, unhindered by his shackles.

The shower/toilet chair is massive, electric chair like. It seats the twin over the toilet and under the shower. The shower is the most basic of systems and water pressure is crap, so Lou shakes it over the twins to wash them. Shower time is carefully planned with music. Lou finds Ted's nursery rhymes CD and Wheels on the Bus kicks in.

While Ted is safely in the sling, Lou stretches out her arms and limbers up like a boxer before the next round starts, she knows what's coming. As battle commences, Lou gets closer to getting Ted in the prime position to get him in the seat. Ted is thrashing, laughing and his leg tone is extremely tight – Ted is fully extended now like a gymnast finishing his parallel bars, landing on the crash mat, his head on the head rest and bottom touching the base but the rest of his body is fully arched in hysterics, laughing and spitting. Lou needs to break the position from fully extended to a seated position. Not easy but she will not lose this battle.

As she tries to break the plank like pose, Ted's smile gets wider teeth clenched and smiling lips, as he knows the battle is now on. Lou attempts to push his hips into a 90-degree seated position to get Ted into the seat and safely strapped. She feels the strength draining from her arms and her feet slipping on the tiled floor. As she pushes with her final grain of strength, her back and body give up and she slips backwards, hard onto the tiled floor. Ted goes into hysterics and as Lou lands on the small of her back, her mother's instincts kick in and she grips Ted as tight as she can to protect his head but hers smacks the floor. Lou's eyes close and her lips tighten, grimacing. Ted is safe but his hysterics make his tone even stiffer, his body longer and he lays writhing on the floor his back arched. Now in pain, Lou slowly eases him off her, trying to protect her face from Ted's flailing arms.

Lou breathes deeply and her eyes are still closed. Her head throbs, her back is sending shooting pains from head to toe, and she struggles to move. The pain is excruciating. Holly is still shouting; Ted is beside himself. Lou stretches her body flat to the ground. She can't move and looks across at Ted lying on the floor. He is in the foetal position now ; his tone reduces, and he looks back at her and for a fleeting moment, looking genuinely concerned as their eyes meet. He stops laughing and his emerald, green eyes look back at Lou with compassion. A look so rare. His tone lessons and Ted brings his arm across to Lou clumsily and loosely wraps it round Lou's neck.

Lou closes her eyes in pain with her boy's arm still around her and his fingers trying to hold Lou's head. His brain injury won't allow his fingers to gently hold anything. Fingers moving in his open hand or a full-on fist clench so hard it cannot be undone are the only options. With her eyes closed, Lou has flashbacks of that night. The beeps, the blank faces, voices, and the machines. Bizarrely, the colour of the bloody walls. Lou opens her eyes and looks at Ted again, thinking back to what could have been and how have they ended up here on the fucking floor at the foot of the stinking toilet. Lou would do anything to have a ten-minute conversation with her undamaged boy. What would that conversation be like? What would it be about? What would his first girlfriend be like? She imagines the laughs they would have had...Lou savours the moment before lifting Ted's arm off of her. He grabs her hair and it all starts again. Shooting pains fire down her back and down her legs as she attempts to move Ted. She just prays that she can move and that she has not exacerbated her old back injury from years of lifting, kneeling, twisting, and moving the twins.

As Lou gets herself sat up, she shouts through the grimaces and reassures Holly that she will be with her shortly. Lou painfully twists he broken body to get Ted safely away from the loo brush. She cannot fully twist so she slowly manoeuvres herself to her knees, levering herself up with her arms using the toilet and the hoist to lift herself up.

Lou is stooped over like a 90-year-old. She shuffles over to the medicine cabinet and pops on more of her painkillers than usual and applies her back spray. She needs to get Ted off the floor. He is now shouting with the realisation of the situation. It is now dawning on Ted that this is not normal, and he wants to get off the floor and probably change the CD.

The shower-sling is wrapped around the hoist, shower chair, toilet, and Ted. Lou starts the task of untangling the puzzle. She slowly manages to get the hoist untangled and lowers herself, in pain, with the untangled sling to secure Ted back into his sling.

Ted returns to his usual mischievous self, writhing on the tiled floor and hitting out.

Lou is in trouble with her back and the painkillers are not taking the edge off. Every movement drives sharp stabbing down her lower back. As the slings finally gets into position, Lou lowers the hoist down to loop Ted safely in. Lou levers herself back to her feet. Ted is then hoisted in the air and lowered over the chair. Lou puts Plan B (or operation current buns) into action to get Ted over the loo and calm. Lou puts on his favourite track – Five Current Buns is cranked up on the CD player. Lou counts and goes through Ted's list of favourite people to distract him.

Finally, Ted's tone is reduced, and Lou lowers him down, brings across the waist strap, while singing Five Current Buns and gets him securely waist strapped into the shower chair, brings over the shoulder straps wincing in pain. Lou breathes a massive sigh of relief and looks at herself in the mirror, pain is etched on her face.

Lou can now check Holly and change the channel. Putting on Postman Pat, she reassures Holly is well and walks steadily back into the bathroom.

She can now wheel Ted into the walk-in shower. As she turns the shower on, Lou is stood bolt upright like she has a broom stick up her t-shirt and down her tracky bottoms tucked into her Crocs. Lou is worried how she will cope without free movement in her back, but that is a worry for a later time. This is a three-person hoist and doing it alone is just so hard with a strong back, it is now extremely unsafe for the twins and Lou.

As Lou finishes showering Ted, she dries him through the pain and wheels the wet chair back through the house to the dining room and will only risk one transfer back to the safety of the table. Ted is being very compliant; he understands not the implications of his actions but that his mum is in pain and doing all she can. It's a rare moment of compliance.

When he is safely in his chair, Lou slowly wheels Ted to be with Holly and changes the channel back to CBeebies. Lou puts a call into the agency to find out what's going on and why the lunchtime carer hasn't shown up. On hold for 10 minutes, she gives up. Lou just prays the evening carer will arrive to give her some respite. She shouldn't but takes another two pain killers. Lou is determined not to ring the duty social worker as this will be a green light for social care to take the twins into care. A moment of weakness will be all social care need to get the twins condemned to the horrors of residential care and pull the plug on all and any home care. A care home in Covid would be a death sentence for her babies. Lou knows she is alone and will just have to suck it up.

Lou reluctantly explains to Holly that she will only be able to change and shower her on the changing table today which isn't great but in with her back in bits, she does not trust herself to do the transfer alone. Lou does all she can to get Holly as clean as possible and dresses her, but her pain extends the time for Holly to half an hour and both Holly and Lou are incredibly frustrated by this.

Holly is safe so, tentatively, Lou lowers herself down to a seated position on a chair with four cushions. She puts her head in her hands and takes a moment. In moments like this Lou wonders where her life is going and thinks about Jake and Megan. Through the tears, Lou knows she shouldn't ever compare because she loves the twins unconditionally but often wonders what life would have been like with just her two older children. Would Ben and Lou have made it? Jake and Megan were such bouncy, confident, and outgoing children before the twins came along. Too young to really understand but, young enough to know that this was life changing and not for the better – they were never the same again after that night.

Lou looks out of the window and notices a robin bobbing along the fence. It appears to look back at Lou, for a brief moment the world stops. The two of them are just there, staring at each other through the window. Lou is transfixed by the robin who looks straight at her as if to say; *I know, be strong, be resilient and positive.* When Lou was young and out walking with her grandmother, the kind old lady would point out the friendly robin bobbing along with them as they walked, saying it was the spiritual form of her mother looking over her. Lou had never forgotten this and took a sliver of comfort dwelling on these brief moments, thinking of the wonderful carefree times at her grandmother's.

With a last bob, the robin flies away. That about sums up the very problem Lou finds herself in; most of the people in Lou's life can just fly off from this situation like so many of her friends and family. So many kind but hollow, empty words and excuses, virtuous grandstanding but very little 'in the trenches' effort to support Lou. To holiday with Lou and the twins meant completely adapting the holiday around the care regime. Nobody had actually done this, ever. There had been much 'oh yes it would be great to go away,' and 'let's have a look at it' over the years. Only for her closest friends and family to disappear off without Lou and the twins or with each other, excluding Lou and her baggage. She'd see on social media that they had gone away again without her. Thanks HUN! She got used to it. At first it hurt; it was gut-wrenching. Lou would now look at the pictures and just think, *actually I'm glad I'm not there*. The build-up was always better than the actual event. Normal holidays, so many barriers for the disabled family that it was actually better to stay here with the gear in place to live.

Her ability to cope was waning. A carer, social worker, cleaner but mostly a tired cynic and now bitter about her life and the cards that she had been dealt. Then, as she has done so many times, she shakes herself down, gives herself a pep talk and, unlike the robin, cannot fly away. She can barely walk and needs to get back to it.

Her back is killing her and in severe pain, Lou slowly levers herself up and out of the chair and the throne of cushions, off again for the next shift.

Chapter 20

Staring into the Abyss

It's a lovely sunny spring morning. Birds are singing and the world is still in lockdown, but carers are starting to work again.

As Deppy drives down the quiet road, she pulls up outside the house. The bungalow is looking tired, flaking paint around the windows, broken pots in the garden, weeds are peeping out of every crevice and between the paving.

Deppy puts on her protective outfit, not quite HAZMAT suits anymore, but mask, protective screen, apron, and gloves help to protect. Covid is still a big thing and Deppy, although testing every day, is careful not to spread any potential illness across her portfolio of cared for people.

She's arrived for her morning shift to help getting the twins up. Deppy tries the door, which is usually open but this time it's locked. She starts banging on the door as the bell isn't working. Nothing. Deppy bangs again a little harder. Although a caring person, she is in a hurry to get this shift done and then onto the next one. She walks around to the front window, but the curtains are closed. The house is eerily quiet, just the sound of the birds singing in the trees and the odd car passing.

Now concerned that she will be late, Deppy opens the letter box and cannot hear a thing. Weird.

Deppy shouts through the letterbox 'Lou are you there?'

Peering inside, she cannot see anything so goes round the side of the house. Through a slit in the sitting room curtain, Deppy spots Lou, lifeless on the sofa, bottles of alcohol and tablets on the table in front of her.

Deppy bangs on the window but cannot wake Lou.

In a panic, Deppy calls Terry the social worker. 'Terry, Terry. It's Deppy. I am at Lou's and cannot get in, Lou's passed out on the sofa.'

'I am on way, stay there.'

Luckily Terry was on his way into work and not that far away. Knowing what state Lou's mind has been in at the moment, thoughts bounce around in Terry's head. He is racing to get to Lou's side. Terry screeches to a halt outside the house and Deppy is at the front looking out for him. 'Terry I am so glad you're here. Have you got your key?' Deppy greets him.

Terry leans into the door and drives it open with his shoulder. The house is in total darkness and completely quiet. Terry and Deppy walk slowly down the cluttered dark hall into the living room where Lou is passed out.

'Lou, Lou, wake up – please Lou.' Deppy kneels down next to her.

Terry shakes Lou around the shoulders. 'Lou, it's Terry. Please wake up.'

As Terry tries to wake Lou, Deppy surveys the room. It's connected to the kitchen and is basically like a one-bedroom flat. It is obvious Lou has been living in this area. The room has a strange smell, a mixture of soiled nappies, sour milk, sweat, old food and alcohol. Equipment, boxes, bags, full nappy bins, and medical paraphernalia are everywhere. Deppy knew it had been going downhill, the signs were there, but she had spent some time back home in Greece after travel restrictions were lifted, and Terry had been so busy he hadn't been able to make it. So, Lou had been flying solo for what had seemed an eternity, part abandoned, part given up on herself and the situation. Deppy and Terry was frantically trying to piece together the scene.

The table in front of Lou was cluttered with a mixture of feeding syringes, empty cups, plates, snack, packets and, alarmingly, medication. Lots of medication. A mixture of Lou's pain killers, sleeping pills and others and the twin's epilepsy medication. Empty foil capsule packets are strewn across the table with empty bottles of red wine and gin.

With Terry still shaking her shoulder, Lou slowly starts to come round. Her eyes are sunken back in their sockets, hair matted from the overnight sofa surfing. A blanket is half on and half off showing her usual saggy, sweat-stained t-shirt and baggy tracky bottoms that it seems haven't been changed for days. Dust particles dance on the light shining through the slit in the curtain. The sun bounces off Lou's face as she hides her eyes from the shimmering light reflecting off the bottles and foil on the table.

'Lou, where are the twins? What's happened?' Deppy asks.

Wearily, Lou replies, 'the twins, in bed I think.'

Her eyes are totally glazed over, and she can hardly keep them open. They have lost any sparkle, a mixture of cigarette stain yellow and redness. Lou is struggling to speak clearly.

Lou was riddled with pain from her back, wrists, and arms. Constant headaches and chronic back pain were blocked out by heavy medication. Lockdown had badly affected Lou and it was obvious that she had stopped looking after herself to just stay alive and give the twins what they needed. The quicksand had finally enveloped her.

The twins' sound monitors were strangely silent. The red power button winked but no sound came out, just a strange echo and the screens were off.

Terry walks slowly down to the twins' room, passing Lou's bedroom with curtains shut and a neatly made bed that looked like it hadn't been slept in for weeks. There are cardboard boxes strewn across the floor in the corridor along with clothes and discarded disposable feeding tubes and used feeding sets. Empty formula milk bottles were everywhere. Terry opens the twins' door which had been battered by equipment and wheelchairs going in and out. Terry is joined by Deppy following closely behind.

There are the twins lying in bed, motionless, curtains closed. The feed pumps are off, and the twins are just lying there in their Teletubbies and Barbie branded bedding. There night fan is on to keep the twins cool, blowing their hair backwards and forwards as it rotates around the room.

Deppy pleads with Terry, 'are they OK?'

Terry walks to the beds and checks the twins' hands – they are cold.

Terry's puts his hand over his mouth and Deppy peers around Terry's broad shoulders. Tears appear in Terry's eyes as he looks at the ceiling, still holding his mouth. As he does, Deppy checks on Holly who is tightly constrained by her night lying board – an archaic wooden and foam looking contraption to keep her safe at night. Bookends under the armpits, hips and both legs tightly hold Holly on her back and safe. Strapped in with Velcro – it looks like a contraption bye-gone age. Holly's pillow was strangely lying on the bed on her legs on top of her quilt.

Holly is motionless with her eyes slightly open. Deppy cups Holly's cheek. The coldness of it runs through Deppy like an electric shock.

Deppy turns to Ted. His head is tilted away, and his body, constrained by his lying board, is tightly packed in, arms flopping down. Deppy holds Ted's hand which for the first time in his life is floppy and soft. His usual high muscle tone is gone.

Ted's cushion hangs partly under his head and partly off the bed at an angle. Lou staggers into the room and Terry springs around. 'No, Lou! Go back to the lounge. We will deal with this.'

Terry manhandles Lou by the shoulders and turns her

back out of the room. As he does, he turns to Deppy and says, ‘Call 999.

Chapter 21
The Darkest Hour

'999, what's your emergency?'

'Ambulance quick, please.' Deppy stumbles over her words. 'The twins, the twins. I need help.'

'Is the patient breathing?'

'No, No.'

'Can you tell me what's happened?'

'The twins, they are in bed and aren't moving.'

'OK, stay calm for me – are they breathing?'

'No.'

'Right, your category one. We will get someone there for you as soon as we can. How old are they do they have any Covid symptoms? Let's start doing chest compressions. Are you ready?'

No, no Covid symptoms. They are not breathing. Please come quickly!'

'We are very busy, but you are a category one. The crews have been informed and will be with you as soon as they can.'

Deppy shouts for Terry to come quickly she needs help. Terry is sitting Lou down on a chair in the kitchen. Lou is now beside herself with worry making no sense at all shouting , 'my babies, my babies.'

In the bedroom, Deppy rolls the covers back off Holly's floppy, fragile body.

Deppy continues her conversation with the operator. 'What do I do now?'

'Have you done chest compressions before?'

'Er, yes, in training, on a dummy.'

'Right, listen to me. We are going to press down on the chest on the sternum. Do you know where this is?'

'Yes, chin downwards and find the sternum.' Deppy repeats what she learned during her training.

'Seal your mouth over their mouth and blow steadily and firmly for about one second. Check that their chest rises. Give two rescue breaths. We are going to continue with cycles of 30 chest compressions and two rescue breaths until they begin to recover or until emergency help arrives.'

Terry comes into room and closes the door. 'What are we doing, Deppy? Giving mouth to mouth?'

'Yes,' she confirms.

Terry goes back-to-back with Deppy and leans over Ted, throwing back the bedding with its smiling characters on and goes straight into chest compressions.

Lou bursts into the room sobbing and cannot believe what's she is walking into. 'Oh no, no, no.'

Lou stands at the end of the room with head in her hands, running her hands through her hair and onto the top of her head. 'My babies, my babies.' Bedraggled and shaking, Lou shuffles around in circles at the doorway.

Terry and Deppy continue their life saving effort with mobile phone on loudspeaker on table between the twins. Gastronomy feed pumps still connected to the twins' tummies and are still ticking over. Terry disconnects the tube away and, as he does, the pump fires milk out, spewing the white liquid across the walls as it continues to pump like a heartbeat.

Deppy and Terry do all they can with each twin. The

bedroom is more like an emergency room than a child's bedroom. They continue the resuscitation, waiting for the paramedics to arrive while the phone operator continues to talk them through the resuscitation process and keep them up to date with the ambulance's progress, making its way across the city in heavy traffic.

Both children are still limp and lifeless, blue lips and look like rag dolls in their wooden lying boards.

Terry shouts to Lou, 'Please go and get the paramedics when they arrive. Go, go now!'

Deppy finally breaks and tears are streaming down her face. Her attempts to resuscitate become weaker and weaker, her head now bowed over Holly's lifeless body.

Terry can hear the faint whine of sirens and, as it gets closer, looks up at the door waiting for the professionals to take over and bring these kids back to life.

Paramedics arrive and walk down the hallway like Sherpas, their backs stacked with green bags, holding holdalls, and talking on their walkie talkies.

They arrive to a horrific scene. They ask for as much background information as they can in the seconds they have to get to work. Deppy slips to the back of the room and Terry tells them all they need to know.

Lou comes to the door, her hair suspended by her hands, mascara and tears streaming down her cheeks.

The Paramedics attach their electronic equipment, the beeps and blips send Lou into an even more anxious state, remembering that fateful night. Terry walks Lou out of the room and into the kitchen.

'Lou, what on earth has happened? What happened last night?' Terry asks.

'I don't know, I really don't know.' Lou whispers. 'I must have passed out.'

'What did you take? Were you drinking Lou?'

'I don't know Terry; I just don't know.'

Terry then asks the question he never thought he would be

asking. He lifts Lou's chin up and looks her straight into her eyes. 'Did you try and take your own life?'

Silence. Lou looks out of the window. Her crumpled face is twisted in grief. 'Terry, not now, please,' she says. 'I need to get back to the twins.'

'Lou, stay here, let the paramedics do their work, they are doing all they can.'

Deppy walks into the kitchen in a daze, cheeks covered in make-up and tears, and slumps into a chair.

The door to the twins' room is blocked by green-suited paramedics, as there are now two crews on site. Lou stares out of the kitchen towards the twins' room and can hear the bips and blips coming from behind the green suits.

There is an eerie silence and then more sirens can be heard coming down the street, more crews arrive along with the fast response unit with a senior paramedic. The senior paramedic walks past the assembled emergency team in the twins' bedroom and appears to be asking questions, a lot of questions, and then turns back to the room. 'Who's mum?'

Terry points to Lou and she puts up a shaky hand.

'We are now working on the children. My name is Mark. Is there a DNR in place?'

'A DNR?' Lou asks.

'Do not resuscitate!'

'Do not resuscitate?!' What, no! Why would there be?'

'No problem, we have to ask. Thank you. Leave this with us.'

Mark then turns his back and goes past the green-suited cordon at the door.

More personnel arrive, and a policeman and Terry directs them to the room which is now full of varying levels of paramedics who spill out into the corridor.

Behind the team huddle are the lifeless twins.

The policeman talks into his radio, walking into the living room. The officer surveys the room, which looks like half drug den, half hospital storage room.

Lou is being comforted in the kitchen by Terry and Deppy, still dazed, confused, and desperately upset.

One by one, the paramedics turn away from the bedroom and slowly walk down the hall with their bags and boxes, packing equipment away. The senior Paramedics takes control and is looking at his watch.

Terry knows what's coming and his body starts to tense up. Then he hears it; 'Time of death.' All agreed.

Terry slides closer to Lou, ready for the reaction as he knows it coming. The senior paramedic turns to the assembled group in the kitchen, fixing his eyes on Lou. 'Mum?'

'Yes.'

'We have done all we can and there is nothing more we can do.'

Lou screams hysterically, it's a primal scream – loud and screechy – and falls to the ground on her knees. Deppy and Terry lower themselves, surrounding Lou and putting supportive arms around her. Lou is broken.

Mark patiently and compassionately stands at the side of the huddled group on the floor, waiting to talk.

Terry stands ups up. 'What happened?'

'The team did all they could, but it was too late. The children had passed some time ago.'

'How did they die?'

'We won't know until the autopsy, but they were unresponsive.'

'But how, how could they both die?' Terry asks again.

'We won't know just yet.'

The policeman is stood in the doorway and addresses the group. 'We will need to take statements from all of you in a moment. Can I just have some time alone with the paramedics?'

Terry, Lou and Deppy then leave, going to the lounge. The twins' bedroom door is now shut.

The policemen, Mark and another paramedic are now locked in the Kitchen talking. Nearly an hour passes as the gathered group in the kitchen make their notes. Another two police officers arrive and go into the kitchen.

Eventually, the three officers walk into the lounge and inform Deppy, Terry and Lou that they will all need to come to the station.

This has taken a sinister twist.

Lou looks at the officers. 'I need to be with my babies.'

'I am sorry, but you cannot be with them as this is now a crime scene due to the circumstances of their death.'

All three just stare at the police, opened mouthed. '*Crime scene*'.

'Scene of the crime investigators are on their way, and we will deal with the bodies which will be taken to the coroner.'

Lou screams. 'I need to see them.'

'I am really sorry, but you need to come with us on a voluntary basis to give a statement.' Looking at Deppy and Terry, the officer adds, 'You need to come with us also.'

Deppy is worried about her other clients. 'Can I ring the office please?'

'Sure, be quick,' The officer says.

Then all three are marched to three different cars and three more officers arrive.

The house is a full-on crime scene as the three of them are driven to the central police station.

The bedroom and the lounge are cleared and taped off. Scene of the crime officers starts to arrive and check in, putting on their white suits, blue overshoes, and masks.

The room is peaceful with the twins as they were left by the paramedics, quilts pulled up to their chins and tucked into the underside of the lying boards. No bips, no beeps, no life. Just the clicking and flashing of the camera. SOCO's get out their swabs and metal cases with various liquids, dust, and fingerprint Perspex. Laying out their paraphernalia, they add squares to the floors for the bodies to be removed without touching the crime scene.

The SOCO's and forensic pathologists continue their work, painstakingly going over the scene, taking prints off every piece of equipment, button, and piece of medical kit in the room. The bodies are checked and then carefully black bagged ready to be taken back to the lab.

The SOCO's continue with their investigation. They open the curtains in the rooms, carefully checking for fibres or any evidence to piece together what has led to this situation.

As the bodies are taken from the house, a group of neighbours have assembled on the road, some filming what has happened. Neighbours that have probably never spoken to Lou, dropped in or even know the twins' names. As they filter off back to their normal lives, they twitter away about what they speculate has happened. A single neighbour who had seen the bodies being loaded into the plain black van had been to her garden and cut flowers, binding them together with brown string with a label with the words.

We didn't know each other; my thoughts and prayers are with you xx

As the procession of officials leaves, the house is locked down, all the curtains shut, doors taped off with a single policeman stationed at the door to protect the scene. The police know that to some twisted elements of society would want to get into to film the scene and add to their social media portfolio of crime scenes with their speculations and theories.

Terry is sat in the back of the Police car, passing familiar sights, Trent Bridge, Meadow Road and over the Canal Street roundabout through the passing shoppers and commuters. His mind runs over the scene. He asks to open the window as he is now starting to panic for Lou, thinking what an earth must have happened. Running through every scenario in his mind, he prays it was natural causes but knows the chance of this for both twins would be millions to one. He thinks about work and texts, saying he won't be in; Terry is a key witness as one of the first on scene.

Deppy cries all the way to the police station, sobbing

deeply into her sleeves. She asks the drivers what will happen next, and the officers say very little. Deppy is in a daze and just wants what she has just seen to be undone. She cannot unsee the children lying in bed, lifeless and limp. The children were so full of noise and life in their own way. Their excessive movement, laughter, and shouting, there was never a dull moment. Seeing them lying lifeless was just so hard to comprehend for Deppy, a natural carer and kind person. She had cared for her mother in her final years and her aunty. She had seen death and the final moments of life. These were children though; this was tragic and not a natural end to a full life. The twins' life had been tragically cut short – but how? Deppy can think of nothing else but the twins.

Lou's journey is very different. She's dazed and confused. There are no more tears, and she just stares out of the window, watching the passing landscape. Her brain is frazzled. She didn't get a goodbye kiss with her babies and thankfully didn't see the children leaving in body bags. Images of the twins' life flash through her mind; bringing them home, birthdays, that moment with Ted on the bathroom floor, the laughs, singing nursery rhymes, school plays all flashing back through her mind. It felt like a Kineograph animation flip book. The end still didn't feel like it had happened. The twins were still with her.

As they pull up to the police station, Lou can see Terry getting out of police car being led thought the back door. He looks back, no smile, no wave – just blank. Lou returns his blank expression. Both perplexed by what had transpired that morning. Still in her pink pinstriped uniform with her name badge on, Deppy looks straight forward as she is also led through the back door. Lou is held back until they are safely inside, segregated and away from both. The police cannot have any more communication between the three.

Once the yard is clear, the officers get out of the car and open Lou's door and help her out. Lou is led across the yard, head down and through the doors, no handcuffs. The station is tired, a mixture of brown stained carpet tiles, white suspended ceiling, and battered magnolia walls. Lou is taken to a room while a female officer takes her clothes and replaces one tattered dirt grey tracksuit for another clean tracksuit. Lou is then led out of the room by the officer with the next stop being an interview room.

The room is classic 80's; pale blue in colour, dark blue worn out carpet to a single plastic village hall chair opposite two chairs for the interviewing detectives. Lou is asked to sit. The mahogany table has been engraved by worried interviewees and a tape machine waits to record every word. The officer leaves, letting Lou know that two detectives will be with her shortly. Lou is left on her own. No shouting, no CBeebies, no Knees Up Mother Brown, no Makaton Five Current Buns. Silence.

She looks around the room at the high-level frosted window, allowing no view of the outside, CCTV red light flashing in the corner and a large mirror at one end of the room. Lou sits and waits, arms down by her side just looking at the wall.

The door opens with a bang, which jolts Lou. Lou immediately asks the arriving officer how the twins are. Both detectives look at each other. The detectives introduce themselves as Raj and Tina, caution Lou and press record on the tape recorder. Two red lights pop on and two green lights go back and forth as the detectives talk.

They ask Lou about the events of the previous day. Lou talks them through what she can remember. The morning, getting up as normal. Deppy arriving, texting Megan and Jake. She remembers that Jake hadn't replied - Megan had. Lou talks about lunchtime; grabbing a sandwich, the children sat watching TV and listening to songs. Lou remembers not going out and having a break in the garden at some point. The afternoon then becomes hazy. Lou talks about her back being in pain and the twins being very unsettled in the afternoon as physio had been stopped and the children appeared to be in pain but could not tell Lou where it was, and she couldn't identify what was hurting. This made their muscle tone worse, and she remembers Ted hitting out a lot.

Lou's memories get fuzzier. She can remember taking a glass or two – she can't remember exactly how many – into the garden to escape the incessant shouting from the twins and take the edge off the day. Raj and Tina leap on this period of time like bloodhounds. This is the one that most worries them. Lou talks about drinking a couple and cannot coherently put together the day's events after lunch. 'Did anybody come to the house?' the detective asks. Lou cannot remember anyone arriving. The detectives probe deeper; 'did you receive any deliveries that day?' Lou cannot remember as she gets a lot of deliveries with medical supplies, nappies, medication, and various other twins-related bits of kit. Lou cannot confirm or deny if there were any deliveries on the afternoon but does remember the postman delivered some mail in the morning.

Lou remembers taking her pain killers as her back was extremely painful but cannot confirm how many. They talk about other medication and Lou admits to taking sleeping tablets sometimes if she was in extreme pain. This day was one of those days. Between the alcohol and the tablets, her day drifted by all the way to when she was found. The probe continues as to what the twins did in the afternoon. Lou talks about going in the garden briefly with one of the twins but was struggling to push them over the steps with her pain. How many bottles did she drink? Lou was probed. There was more than one bottle on the table and an empty bottle of vodka, but Lou's memory is hazy, and she can't confirm or deny that she has had more than one. There were three empty bottles of wine on the table, more in the kitchen and at the back of the house and three quarters of the bottle of vodka gone and more of them at the back of the house. There were many empty foil packets of Tramadol, Temazepam and Triazolam. Lou could not confirm how many she had taken and only that her last memory was putting the twins to bed after their personal care. The detectives ask why the CCTV watching them was off and why she hadn't been to bed. Lou cannot remember but says she never went to sleep without the CCTV, had fallen asleep on the sofa and thinks she was watching TV. This was normal, she didn't always go to bed. They press on about visitors in the afternoon or evening. Lou cannot recall. 'How long did you sleep for?' they ask.

Lou cannot remember at all after putting the TV on and the twins safely in bed, feeds on and fan on. The questioning goes on for an hour and a half and Lou is all over the place, trying to piece together the night. The days and nights have merged into one set of blurry events. It was obvious that Lou was fast asleep, heavily sedated by the booze and the tablets. Lou was now riddled with guilt and grief.

Lou has no answers, and this has neither gone well or badly as there is such a massive uncorroborated amount of time. But she had a duty of care and that is central to this tragedy.

Raj and Tina bring the interview to a close, stop the tape and inform Lou she will be held while they make further enquires. Lou is led out of the room by an officer to a holding cell. The door slams shut, and the small porthole is opened and shut. That was it.

Lou sits on the plastic mattress and puts her head in her hands trying to understand the last 24 hours. Carefully piecing together, the hours that have passed in this whirlwind of mixed-up memories. The last few weeks and months have blurred into one version, the reoccurring days of care had manifested themselves into a false belief that last night was just another night and Lou was present throughout. She builds up a story in her mind and that the twins must has passed naturally as everything had been 'just another night.' Lou pulls her knees up, wraps her arms around her legs and drops her head into her knees. She sits in this pose for hours. The CCTV light flashes in the corner and the custody sergeant just watches this grieving mother sat in a lonely cell with no one. Her twins were her life and the shock of what has happened was sinking in. The sergeant watches intently to ensure Lou gets though the day until she is re-interviewed.

Raj and Tina go to the mortuary to speak to the forensic pathologists and gather all they can from SOC officers and detectives who have pieced together what they can in the short time they have had. The team get buzzed in and walk through reception into the huge boardroom overlooking the laboratory. As they are welcomed in, the forensic pathologists go through their findings.

The twins have died through asphyxia, probably caused by being suffocated with their pillows which has traces of their DNA on and saliva. The obvious question was about other DNA or fibres. Who would use pillows to suffocate the twins? Tina tries to weigh up why a mum whose children had suffered hypoxia at birth and effectively starved of oxygen, suffocating the life out of them, would put them through it again? It doesn't add up, but Lou had no answers. As the forensic breakdown of the crime scene continued, Lou's DNA, prints and fibres were everywhere so that really did not help. There were other prints, which it turned out belonged to Terry and Deppy. Megan and Jake's prints were around the house and so were Ben's. It really didn't help the situation as there were no foreign prints. As they piece together the lounge, most of the prints were Lou's but Terry's were present on some of the glasses and empty bottles of alcohol. But that didn't necessarily put him there the night before. The cameras were off so there was focus on the power controls and how and who turned them off. Terry and Deppy made statements, and the cameras were a constant. Terry and Deppy had explained their whereabouts and were on the watch list but were confirmed as not on the scene. Deppy was working and then home with her family. Terry was on a work night out and out until late and then his Ring cameras were used to confirm his arrival home and not leaving the house until the morning.

Other doorbell and CCTV camera footage had been viewed by the detectives who were bust piecing the day together.

As the pathologist goes through the rest of the evidence

and the end of the twins' lives, they discuss time of death which they identify as being between 10pm-12am. This band of timing was in the larger band where Lou cannot recall whether she was awake or asleep. The only definite was putting the twins to bed but this was blurry as this was just part of her routine. Although they have cause of death, this does not move them forward with who and when this happened. Tina and Raj get up and leave, as they do they peer through the glass and see the twins in the morgue with white sheets pulled up to their chins. The twins' pale, lifeless, and still faces, eyes closed. Stillness is all they see after a life of Athetoid Cerebral Palsy, uncontrolled movement and tense muscles, their injured brains still for the first time since they were in the ICU in Liverpool. That is all they see. It's heart-breaking for them both and humbling. They have work to do and will not stop until they find out who did this and why.

Lou remains the number one suspect, but they need concrete evidence to progress and interview again.

Chapter 22

Lines of Enquiry

Raj and Tina's investigation continued and there were three strong lines of enquiry:

> *Ben and his business dealings and the threats he had been receiving.*
>
> *Lou, mum as the only one on scene.*
>
> *Carers and family.*

The house had 5 key-holders.

Lou, Terry, Megan, Jake, Ben – all were suspects as Lou was not present, they needed to know the movements of the previous day. Who, if anybody, visited the house?

As the team widened their investigation to the neighbours, studying CCTV, interviews, and doorbell cams, they delved deeper into previous 24 hours and the events leading up to and following the tragic events.

As they ponder the board in the office with names, pictures, and timings, they get a call from Tom in the corner of the office.

'Boss, watch this.'

Tom throws up the grainy image up onto the projector at the end of the office. A neighbour over the road caught on his dated CCTV guarding his precious Swift caravan an evening arrival at the house. The house was in darkness and a white van passes the house five times before slowly pulling up on the road in front of the house.

The occupants of the van sit for 14 minutes, making calls, and then one of them comes out of the van with a small box. It looks to be an Amazon delivery. What's bothering the junior detective is that there is a driver and a driver's mate which is extremely rare. They are hooded and masked, all in black. As the driver's mate gets out of the van with his box, the driver gets out, also on his phone. Both are obscuring their faces. The driver then stands at the door on his phone looking out up and down the road. The 'delivery' is taken round the back of the house by the driver's mate. They are at the house for 15 minutes or so which is very suspicious, and the driver's mate then comes back with the box. This is of real interest to the detectives as Ben had been receiving death threats.

Ben's financial issues had been a massive worry for the family. His biggest gamble was through his uncle Frank; the investment in the Manchester property deal with its huge, ratcheted stage payments with the promise of huge profits at the end had all made sense in his eyes. Until he stopped paying on the agreed dates.

The Albanian gang had built up a fierce some reputation in Manchester, the drug dealers were a zero-tolerance outfit. They were desperately trying to accelerate their whole outfit to legitimise themselves with property and business investments. The 40 barber and sweet shops had to be scaled down. They were clearly money laundering outfits, and the heat was definitely on with the net closing in on the gang, so their transition needed to happen and happen now. Missed stage payments were crippling the outfit and one late payment could be tolerated but three missed payments meant punishment.

It was an honour thing and they needed to keep up their reputation.

Ben had reported the 'anonymous' death threats to the family. Nobody was ever convicted or interviewed as it was not clear 'within law' who had sent them.

This was on file and drew Tina and Raj's attention to this weird "Amazon delivery".

Uncle Frank was one of the gangs most trusted associates who had fingers in all sorts of pies, some legit but most not. His black book was significantly thick, and he had overstretched the book this time, so everybody had to pay the full amount and on time. Frank had got Ben involved in the most recent scheme, the biggest scheme of all. Frank had held back the gang for as long as he could from dealing directly with Ben.

Ben had gone to ground, hiding out at Hetty's, and was working sporadically at different offices on different days so the gang wouldn't know his whereabouts. Ben knew they were staking the bungalow out and if he showed up there it would be goodbye.

Lou had concerns after getting various house phone calls pre-lockdown asking for Ben and unknown people to her arriving at the bungalow looking for Ben. They would never leave a name or any other details. What Lou did know was that these people not the kind of characters Ben would normally mix with. They were very keen to speak to Ben and it scared Lou as they would arrive at any time of day and evening, and she always said to Terry she felt she was being watched.

As they closely watched the CCTV, Raj and Tina needed the van details and registration, so Tom went off to find this. The suspects were fully masked and fully hooded so impossible to ID. What was clear was that they were not delivering anything and there was a missing amount of time where the second suspect was out of the picture round the back of the house, long enough to murder the children.

The van registration came up blank as it was registered to a BMW. The van was later found burnt on Langar Airfield. A disused and remote airfield, the chances of witnesses is going to be very unlikely.

The team then tried to piece together the events and through the ANPR cameras to check the movements of the white van after it left the house.

As the CCTV unfolds, there is foot traffic past the unlit house. There are a number of hooded figures that pass the house at various times during the late evening, but the grainy images are not clear. There are a couple of figures that pass the house and one at 11.30pm stops and then walks past but then returns, stops, and looks at the house. Ten minutes later, the hooded figure stops at the path and walks up to the house, at this point a figure then disappears round the back for a period of time but then doesn't return at all. Puzzling.

The figure never re-emerges from the front of the property so from the point where they walk down the path to the property and the next morning when Terry and Deppy arrive there is a huge gap of time. This is crucial.

Raj and Tina then go back to the interview and the keyholders of the property as there appears to be no forced entry. The keyholders including Lou, Ben, Terry, Megan, and Jake. So, the fast-moving enquiry now moves to Ben, Megan and Jake and the teams are sent off to bring in the wider family and, more importantly, the keyholders. But The fake Amazon drivers were not out of the picture yet as the team were not ruling out the house being broken into with skeleton keys.

Ben is first to arrive and is taken straight to the investigation room. Followed by Megan and then Jake. As they arrive, Lou's mum also arrives as an independent parental support. They need an adult in the room who is not associated to the case. Megan and Jake are sat separately in rooms apart.

Ben is first to come in voluntarily with Hetty as one of the next of kin. As Hetty waits outside in the waiting room, Ben is brought in to meet the detectives and give his version of events. It's clear that something happened between 4pm and the time Deppy and Terry arrived the next morning. Ben's face is a mixture of extreme sadness at losing two children, shock and also nervousness at being interviewed under caution. As the team press Ben on his whereabouts that evening and through to the morning, it is clear that Ben was with Hetty all night, they also had two friends round for drinks who would corroborate the story if required. The detectives then moved onto the relationship of the family members with regards to the twins. Ben talks about Lou's drinking which he was aware of as Megan had confided in him about it. Ben had a very distant relationship with Lou due to his relationship with Hetty which made all contact extremely difficult and fraught. He talked about Megan's love and support for the family and the twins. Ben touched on Jake's withdrawal from the family and his lack of love of the twins and that Jake did not spend any time with the twins. He also talked openly about how Jake felt helpless, sad, and angry how their injury had blown the family apart. How he longed for the time before they were born and would do anything to have the family back together without the twins. Ben talked about how he did everything to try and reassure Jake that it wasn't him or his fault that the twins were brain injured and that the staff that had caused or covered up the birth mistakes. Ben says that Jake did get extremely angry with authority figures and distrusted everybody who he associated being in charge or connected to the 'authority'. All he wanted to happen was for the twins to go away and the family to be back to how it was – he talked about this a lot. The detectives felt this was key and wanted to push Jake on this more as this was pretty important to understand Jake's frame of mind.

The detectives then moved on Ben's personal circumstances as they knew he had started a relationship with Lou's sister, and they had found a mass of chasing reminders for cash and bills and notes with threats of violence and worse to the family that Lou had filed in plastic sleeves. They were piecing together a dodgy financial situation and wanted to know who was threatening Ben. As the detectives pushed, he clammed up, but they were not going to let this go and as they started to release the financial statements, final demands, and credit cards bills. Ben started to squirm, and his composure started to break, and he had to explain the last few years and how bad things had got. On the points about who he owed money to, he talked about his friends, but the interrogators knew these loans weren't from friend and family. They pressed, and eventually Ben started to crack. Then they pushed onto phone records, and he started to weep. Then the final shot across the table came, nailing Ben – the name Arkan was mentioned and a Nottingham Forest Game. Ben had unwittingly written down all of the attendees for table settings in hospitality from Manchester including his Uncle Frank, Arkan, and the rest of the band. Ben had doodled on his notes with guns, and someone being shot and the words 'Kingpin' above the heads of a doodled gaggle of thug like characters. Ben had drawn pound values and written dates which appeared to be random but relevant to the investigation. The detectives pushed on this to get as much as they could to build a picture around the unaccounted delivery/non delivery drivers seen on the day to see if their intentions were to send a message to Ben in retaliation for bumping the payments to the gang. Ben's pupils dilated, and he was showing signs of extreme fear when they talked about the gang. The detectives pulled out a few bank statements and then said a forensic investigation was underway of all transactions and mobile and digital exchanges. Ben knew the game was up and it was damage limitation time. After a pause, he came clean without implicating the gang in any wrongdoing. He admitted about the payments and investments into property in Manchester and that his lines of cash had run dry and that he had missed payments and, in the end, stopped payments. He said it was highly likely that associates of the gangs had sent the notes, and they did know where the family lived, but not where Ben and Hetty lived.

'Wow.' The detectives just sat back. This was now a key line of enquiry and put the gang and the drivers front and centre as suspects for the deaths of the twins.

Ben's story was checked out and all seemed to be in order including the friend who corroborated the events of the previous evening.

Megan is led into the interview with a family liaison officer. Her alibi is her grandma as she was staying with her on the night in question.

Megan looks completely blank as she is sat down at the interview table and the tapes start rolling.

'Good morning, Megan. We are detectives Raj and Tina we want to talk to you about last night.'

Megan is aware that her mum is in the station being held and that she has lost her brother and sister and is in a complete state of shock.

The detectives ask Megan where she was last night.

Megan talks about leaving school, being picked up by her grandma, baking, spending time with her grandpa and watching TV. She carefully goes through the programmes they watched together and what time she went to bed.

Asked about leaving the house between going to bed and waking up, Megan confirms that she didn't leave the house and that she got ready as usual, had breakfast, and went to school.

Megan asks what has happened as she is completely lost. She asks to see her mum, which she cannot at this stage which leaves her feeling totally isolated.

Felicity is interviewed and confirms Megan's version of events, so Megan is just about in the clear.

Ben is then asked to go through a formality of identifying the bodies at the morgue. He is met in the morgue waiting room by Ben and Raj and led down the corridor to a room with a huge glass window with a white curtain. As Ben stands against the wall, the white curtain draws open and sympathetically lit and decorated room starts to appear. In the middle of the room are two oversized beds. Two white sheets are tightly wrapped around two bodies. At the heads of the tables are two thick pillows and two angelic faces, eyes closed, pale and lifeless. Ted and Holly, his beautiful children, are laying in front of him with no one there. The twins have had someone by their side from the minute they were born and now are alone separated from each other and their parent and carers.

Ben brings his hands to his eyes; he walks slowly up to the glass and puts his hand on the glass, hunched over and sobbing at his two beautiful children, lifeless. He feels pathetic and weak. Guilt washes over him he cannot believe it has come to this and is no closer to fathoming who on earth would do this to such vulnerable beautiful humans. His flesh and blood who he will never spend time with again. Ben sits down on a chair at the back of the room and asks for a moment of silence. If he had been there, this wouldn't have happened, could he have saved them. Raj checks in on Ben and asks is he wants some water; Ben just shakes his head and Raj gives him some time alone. Ben emerges and hugs Hetty, the two holding an embrace before leaving together. For Raj its back to business and get this case cracked.

Jake is brought into the interview room with his grandma, Felicity, and Tina and Raj are sat waiting. Jake is dressed in Hi-tops, black jeans, and a converse t-shirt. His hair is untidy, he is pale and slightly bedraggled. As they start the tape, they introduce themselves to the family who are without a solicitor at this stage. The tag team start the interview, leaning back to hear what Jake has to say.

'Good afternoon, Jake. We need to talk to you about your brother and sister.'

Jake hardly looks up from staring at the table, his emo, greasy hair hanging over his eyes.

'Jake, we have some bad news, both your brother and sister are dead.'

There's nothing from Jake – totally emotionless.

Felicity puts her hand over her mouth and starts to cry.

'Jake, did you hear what I just said?'

Jake looks up and nods his head.

'Jake, we need to know where you were yesterday.'

Felicity is looking at Jake through the tears.

'Jake?'

Nothing.

'Jake, where were you between the hours of 6pm and 6am yesterday,' the detectives try again. 'Jake?'

Jake just has his head down and then looks up and nods.

'Where were you yesterday?'

Jake then speaks for the first time. 'I was out until 12am and then at my mate's house.'

'Who is your mate? Jake?'

'His name is Caleb; I live with his mum.'

'Where were you?'

'In town.'

'Where abouts in town?'

'At the park.'

'Which Park?'

'Forest recreation ground.'

'What times, Jake?'

'Not sure, after 6pm.'

'How long were you there for?'

'Unsure, but it was dark when we left.'

'Who did you leave with and where to?'

'Back to Caleb's.'

'What time?'

'Dunno.' Jake shrugs.

'We will need to speak to Caleb. Were you with him all of the time, Jake?'

'Yeh.'

'How did you get home?'

'We walked.'

'And you don't know what time you got home?'

'No.'

'Did you visit your mum on the way back, Jake?'

Jake just looks down and doesn't speak, looking edgy.

'Jake?' The detectives probe.

'No.'

Felicity sits there silently. The tears have stopped, and she is staring at Jake and then she asks, 'Jake did you go to see your mum?'

'No, right, I didn't!' Jake snaps.

'OK, we are going to stop it there and speak to Caleb,' Raj says. 'You will be held until we have spoken to him, and the interview is terminated.'

Jake is led to a private secure room with his grandma.

The officers are then despatched to get Caleb and his mum, Sheila.

Caleb walks down the corridor furtively, head down, he looks up to the end of the corridor where Jake is being moved and there is a brief exchange. Caleb is then led to a separate room with Sheila in tow. An officer waits at the door and Raj joins them. The two detectives let Caleb know who they are and then sit down and go thought the formalities of starting the tape and confirming the start time and interviewees and interviewers. Caleb is slumped in his chair, starting at the table. He is desperately anxious on any normal day; so, this process is sending his anxiety through the roof.

As the interview process starts, the detectives hone in on Jake's relationship with his brother ,sisters and parents. Caleb is rattled and starts to say just a little bit too much and the detectives smell blood, pulling out Jake's hatred of his home situation, his disparate relationship with his dad and his lack of attachment to Ted and Holly. The more the detectives push, the more Caleb gives away about Jake's anger at his home situation. Caleb spills his guts all over the interview room and the detectives change tack and hone in on the night in question. As the detectives clarify times and movements, almost all of the story aligns with Jake. Caleb admitted that the group smoked strong weed, took pills and were swigging 'Voddy' most of the night. As they press on the moments when they left the park the story starts to fall apart. They didn't go straight home – together. Caleb says that he actually went home alone, and that Jake followed him later and, in fact, much later. There is a gap in the story after Caleb got home and fell asleep on the sofa and before Jake came back. It does not corroborate with Jakes version of events. As they press Caleb, he goes into a child-like mode, understanding that he could now be in deep trouble for lying. He gives the detectives what they need. The motive was still in question, but it was obvious from the picture being created over the interview that Jake was very angry and carried a lot of resentment towards the twins. He might have done this in a fit of rage, especially if he was under the influence of drugs and alcohol. Or was he acting out a plan he had in his head for years? The cork had finally popped, and he had freed Lou from her life of care and misery. Had he done it to save his mum and, with rose-tinted spectacles on, tried to bring the family back together, back to those halcyon days pre-twins.

The detectives now had a clear line of enquiry and Jake had questions to answer. The delivery drivers had a persona and intent based on the contents of the letters and Ben's massive, massive debts owed to the gang and beyond.

Chapter 23

Unpicking the Evidence

Lou is cautioned and asked if she wants her solicitor or a duty solicitor, she is not sure why or what is going on. As Lou protests that 'She hasn't done anything,' in a daze she asks for a duty solicitor.

Led down to the interview room, Lou is visibly upset and is not sure what is going to happen next or why she is being accused.

Lou is sat down and advised again that she is under caution.

Tina launches straight in, 'Lou tells us about Jake's relationship with you.'

Lou blinks. 'Jake was extremely protective of me when he was younger.'

'Was?'

'Yes. Jake found home life extremely challenging and spent a lot of time away from home. He would only talk about life before the twins arrived.'

'Why is that?'

'He found it very hard to cope and when he was a lot

younger said he wished they weren't here, but this was only a phase he went through when he was young.'

'What did he mean by that?'

'Well, he just preferred it when it was just the four of us.'

'How did Ben get on with Megan?' Tina continues.

'They used to get on well, but Megan was more involved with me, and Jake didn't really spend any time with the twins. Jake did have moments with me and was very empathetic with me. He would ask how I was, and I was very candid about how I felt and how tired I was. He would listen a lot and I probably told him too much. He heard a lot when Ben and I would talk openly about how the twins were injured, our life struggles and how exhausted we both were.'

'Does Jake have a key?'

'Yes, he does.'

'How often does he visit?'

'Jake hasn't been for some time although he does text and WhatsApp now and again.'

'When did he last see you and the twins?'

Lou thinks for a moment. 'Two, maybe three months?'

'OK, and what was Jake's relationship with Ben like?'

'Not great when Jake was young, he idolised his dad and they were inseparable. Ben ensured Jake was the best informed, best dressed and basically the best at everything. But Ben changed and became more and more distant from Jake as our finances worsened and Ben became more distracted by things away from the family and more and more bitter about the establishment itself. He saw how the establishment and authority figures had fought against the family so hard and relentlessly.'

'So, Ben and Jake now, are they talking?'

'No, not really. Jake hasn't seen Ben since he moved in with my sister. It really finished everything off, making a bad situation worse.'

'Had Ben changed?'

'Yes, he's a completely different person.'

'When did he change?'

'We fought the NHS to get answers as we know that mistakes were made and tried to get a legal case against them and get the compensation we deserved.'

'And how did that go?' Tina presses. 'It didn't work out and it really got to Ben, and he changed and didn't cope very well.'

'Why?'

'He looked after the finances and things were not great at the time and he sort of relied on it working out to get our costs back and secure the future for the twins. It really, really set him back and he never really recovered.'

'Back to Jake, Lou. We need to know more about Jake and the night in question. Did you see Jake at all that night?'

'No, I was alone.'

'What about when you were asleep and before?'

'I don't know.'

'We know that you were under the influence of alcohol and prescription drugs. Do you know what you took?'

'No, I am not sure.'

'What time did you fall asleep?'

'I don't know.'

'What can you remember?'

'As I said earlier, I had a few drinks in the afternoon.'

'A few, how many?'

'I don't know. It was glasses of wine and other things. I did take a couple of sleeping pills, but then Ted and Holly were definitely in bed, I remember that. It had been another long day and I remember being in a lot of pain with my back and wrists, so I took some pain killers with the wine.'

'How many?' 'I don't know but I remember it allowed me to get the kids hoisted into bed. I was on auto pilot a bit though and don't think I missed anything and put their feed on and gave them the medication, but I cannot remember exactly – what happened to them. Do we know?'

'Let's stay on the details of the night please.' Tina says. 'Can you remember if you had the TV and radio on?'

'The TV was on, I think, when I fell asleep.'

'What was the last thing you remember watching?'

'The news I think and then The One Show was on and then...that's the last thing I remember...I must have fallen asleep then.'

'So, seven o'clockish was the last time you remember being awake?'

'Yes,' Lou says. 'And I remember looking at the monitor and checking the children.'

'The CCTV was on then?'

'Yes, I think so but all the nights blur into one a bit.'

'Did you get up in the night?'

'No, the next time I woke was when I was woken in the morning.'

'You understand what you're saying don't you?' Tina asks.

'What do you mean?'

'You were the last to see the twins alive and then drank and took pills, but you don't know which ones and how many.'

Lou puts her head in her hands and cries, comforted by the duty solicitor. The detectives wait patiently until Lou composes herself. They are poised to ask the obvious question. 'Lou, we need to ask you. Did you kill the twins?'

'No, no – what are you asking me?' Lou cries.

'You were the only one that we categorically know was in the house at the time the children died. You were exhausted and not in control. You can see how this looks, can't you?'

'Yes but, no – I would never do that.'

'But you were exhausted. Did you kill the children and attempt suicide?' Tina presses.

'No. No, I have thought about it before but have never done it because the twins need me.' Lou shakes her head.

'But if the twins aren't there, they don't need you.'

'No, I guess not. I am just not sure what happened.'

'We will be honest Lou; this isn't looking good; we only have your prints in the house and totally understand how hard it's been for you. Can you see how this looks?' Tina says.

'Have you thought about ending the twins life before to make it all go away?' Raj adds.

Exhausted, Lou doesn't know what to say.

'Yes, well yes as they have had such a tough life and with Covid when will this ever end – it's been so hard,' she says after a long pause.

'My client would like some time please – can we break?' the solicitor cuts in.

The detectives reluctantly have to end the interview.

The detectives then go off to re-group before they tackle another interview with Jake.

Lou and the solicitor go off to another room to try and get more context to what happened that night.

Jake is led from his holding room back to the interview room with Felicity as his guardian, having refused to have his dad with him.

As Tina and Raj enter the room, they are ready for a showdown with his conflicting story.

'Jake we just need to go over the events of the night again if we can please,' Tina starts. 'You say you went home with Caleb after the park?'

Jake nods.

'OK, and then you went back to the house?'

He nods again.

'And do you think that's what Caleb has told us?'

Jake shrugs his shoulders.

'What do you think Caleb's told us?'

'I don't know.' Jake is looking more and more uncomfortable.

'I put it to you, Jake, that you didn't go home when you said, and Caleb went home on his own. You went to your mum's house on that night.'

Jake just shrugs his shoulders.

'Jake, we need to know where you were for those missing hours, where did you go and who were you with?'

Jake just looks down.

'Jake?' Sheila prompts.

'I just walked around Nottingham; I had a spliff.'

'Where did you go?'

'Just around, cannot remember, I think I fell asleep after smoking.' Jake was genuinely unsure. 'Walking through a park, I sat on a bench, I think.'

'Who was with you, Jake?'

'There were people in the park, but I don't know who they were.'

'Boys or girls?'

'Both I think.'

'And then what did you do?'

'I woke up and went back to the house.'

'What time?'

'I dunno.'

'Jake, we need to know where you were, did you go back to your mum's?'

'No.'

'Did you have your key to your mum's with you on that night?'

'No.'

'Jake, did you murder your brother and sister?'

Felicity is now in tears and with her hand over her mouth is sobbing and puts her hand on Jakes shoulder, Jake sits, slouching – navel gazing – emotionless.

'I will ask you again, Jake, did you murder your brother and sister?'

'No.'

'We need to know your exact whereabouts. We have your phone.'

'Jake shrugs.'

Felicity asks if they can stop and talk to a solicitor, so the interview ends, and Jake goes back to his cell.

Raj and Tina go back to the board and consider what they know to date. They have 3 key suspects.

The van drivers connected to the Manchester gang and Ben's evidence. Jake a very angry and disconnected young man who goes missing at the time of the murder. A devastated and exhausted mum at the end of her rope caring alone and all the hallmarks of an attempted mass suicide. The questions now are racing through the detectives' minds, did Jake end his mum's misery knowing that his mum would be out of it? Did the Manchester gang know this was a pattern and that they could break in and give the family a message? Did mum kill the children and then attempt suicide herself which didn't work? The Manchester gang were the outsiders at the moment as there were no prints to anyone unknown in the house, no attempted break-in and it would be extreme to say the least. Ben would more than likely be their target. Jake being a child murderer equally as unlikely. It would be extremely dark and is something the police had never dealt with. So, they are left with Lou who had motive, was found at the scene and but is it beyond reasonable doubt?

The team piece together the information from the interviews and trawl through all the evidence again. They Check the CCTV and go over their notes. Breaking for the day, they know they will need to charge or release the next day – time was up.

Chapter 24
The Truth Will Out

As Raj and Tina arrive the next morning, they are both dreading the day. Both are used to having cases to a point where they have 100% certainty.

They talk to the to the chief superintendent about case progress and explain the next steps. As they run through the case and evidence, even the chief superintendent is on edge. She listens and agrees that they are going to have to charge Lou and release the others. There is simply no clear evidence that the others were at the scene. Jake is released and slopes out of the station and back to Caleb's.

The CPS know now what they have to do and bring Lou in to charge her with her solicitor who has asked that she say nothing, which is pretty easy for Lou as she cannot stop crying. Lou is charged with the murder of her own children, she cannot believe what she is hearing, and her solicitor does all he can to console Lou before asking for time with the client to talk over the next steps. Lou is remanded in custody and will now be held whilst further evidence is gathered to strengthen the case further."ws to Jake that his mum has been charged. Jake's reaction unnerves Sheila who expected home to break down, show some emotion but...nothing.

Jake then smiles and walks away back to his room. Sheila is shocked by this and does not know what to make of it. She doesn't know if it's shock or just adolescent, nonchalant behaviour. Jake then says he is going for a walk and leaves.

Sheila needs to spend more time with him to understand where he is and that he is ok. Jake doesn't come back until late, and Sheila is already in bed. Not sleeping well as this is weighing heavy in her mind she is up with the lark and busies herself until Jake gets up. As he does, Sheila approaches how Jake is feeling but gets little back. She lets him know she is there for him.

Over the coming months, they wait for Lou's trial date. Jake's mood dips significantly and he is going out less and less and smoking more and more weed at home. Sheila is really concerned as the trial date gets closer and closer. Jake spirals, he won't eat and is more and more drawn to weed and gaming. He and Caleb are becoming distant as Caleb continues to go out and socialise. Caleb feels sorry for Jake but cannot reach him, the harder he tries, the further Jake pushes him away. He is so withdrawn by the time the trial date arrives he is now almost totally flat-bound. Sheila has been as lenient and tolerant as she could be, Jake is asking daily when the trial starts, and Sheila has been counting the dates down. Sheila has asked if Jake wants to see his mum and he looks upset by the request and says 'no' he doesn't want to see anybody.

The date then arrives. Sheila makes Jake his daily breakfast bacon cob with lashings of brown sauce and milky sweet tea. As Jake sits on the worktop, Sheila asks Jake if he knows what today is. He says he does and cries. This is the first and only emotion that Jake has shown. This routine goes on through the days of the trial and when Sheila asks if Jake wants to go to the trial to support his mum, Jake refuses.He doesn't want to see his dad or his sister or any family members at all. Sheila is getting increasingly worried about Jake as his diet is any shade of beige, bacon cob breakfast, then energy drinks and brown food. He looks shocking.

The trial lasts over a two-week period with various experts giving evidence trying to piece together the night's events. The trial swings back and forwards and there are a lot of grey areas which the defence picks up on to defend Lou. As the trial comes to an end, the jury are then asked to see if they can come up with a unanimous decision. Jake is asking Sheila a lot of questions as the two weeks start to come to an end and the Jury are deliberating the evidence they have heard.

Sheila gets up one morning and goes through her showering routine and walks into the kitchen in her dressing gown to make a brew and get the grill on for Jake's sandwich. He is sat at the table in tears.

'Hey, hey what's wrong Jake?'

Jake looks up at her, eyes sparkling with tears. 'What's going to happen to mum?'

'I don't know Jake. It's up to the jury now.'

'I just wanted to help.'

'What do you mean?'

'I just wanted it all to go away, back to how it was, when we were a family. Mum cannot go to prison.'

'Jake you're not making sense.'

'I wanted to be how it was before.'

'Before what?'

'Ted and Holly, I hate them.'

'Who? Ted and Holly?'

'The doctors that did this to our family,' Jake says darkly. 'Ted and Holly changed everything; we were happy before them.'

'I know it must have been hard Jake.'

'I just wanted them to be at peace and mum to get better. Mum needs a rest.'

'They are at peace Jake.'

'Yes, but not like this, mum could go to prison, and she

hasn't done anything wrong, I just wanted to help.'

'How do you mean?'

'I needed it all to ok for mum. Ted and Holly should not have been injured, it's the doctor's fault. We were fine before this, and it should never have happened. My dad's a wanker. I want us all back together and now we cannot ever be together because of that wanker shacked up with his sister-in-law. I hate him. I hate what the twins did to us. I did it for mum.'

'What, Jake? What have you done?' Sheila says trepidation in her voice.

'I had to do it. If not, mum would have died and then who would be there to look after Ted and Holly? There would be nobody or they'd ended up being left in a bloody nut house. What life would that of been for them? I needed to free mum and the twins from that. I had to.'

'Jake, you need to tell me what happened.'

'Sheila I am so sorry, I just, just...' Jake stammers. 'I went round to the house.'

'When?'

'On that night. I knew mum would be asleep and out of it. I took my shoes off and went round the back and I could see her on the sofa passed out with the bottles and pills everywhere. I used my key to get in.'

'But there were no fingerprints, how were you not seen?'

'I have a mask and hoodie on and used some of those black gloves, I was very careful. I turned the CCTV off,' he continues. 'I checked mum who was OK, she was so out of it and then went into the twins who were fast asleep. I had to do it Sheila, you know, I just had to.'

Sheila's eyes are wide with shock, but she just waits for him to go on.

'I used a pillow to stop them breathing and end it all for them. All that crying and pain, they couldn't even go to the toilet or eat, you know, Sheila. It was lifetime of misery for them and ending it this way was best for everybody. I didn't want to hurt them or see them, or mum suffer anymore. I had to do it.'

'Then what?' Sheila asks, voice shaking.

'I checked them both and went back to check mum who was still out of it and then went out the back door, locked it, put my shoes back on and walked for a while and then came back. I binned the gloves and the mask and came back here.'

'Jake, we have to tell someone, we need to for your mum.'

'I know, I need to see mum and tell her.'

A massive smile appears across Lou's face as she gets view of Jake arriving in the visitor's room of the prison. As they sit at the table, Jake cannot look his mum in the eye. Sheila sits down besides Jake for support.

'Jake, how have you been darling? It's so good to see you,' Lou says.

'Jake needs to tell you something, Lou,' Sheila prompts.

Jake is simpering, looking down.

'JAKE!!' Sheila nudges him into action.

'Mum, I am sorry.'

'Sorry for what darling, what is it?'

'Mum I am so sorry; I didn't mean for you to go to prison!'

'Darling what do you mean? They have got it wrong.'

'Mum, I Know they have. I just wanted us all to be a family again.'

'We are a family, Jake?'

'No, I mean without Ted and Holly.'

'Jake, don't say that.'

'Mum, I hate them I hate everything I hate what they did to us they ruined everything. They ruined our life.'

'Jake, darling what have you done,' Lou says, trying to look her son in the eye.

'Mum, it was me,' Jake says finally. 'I wanted them to rest, I wanted you to survive!'

Lou is in deep shock. It's emotional overload trying to protect her boy but also absorbing what he is saying he has done to his brother and sister. How could he do this? Lou is overwhelmed with conflicting feelings. How could her son do this to his own siblings?

'Mum, I am sorry. I just didn't want to lose my mum; no one was there for you. Those cunts that did this will not go away. It was doing my head in mum, I had to do something.'

'Mum, what have I done?'

'Jake, you should have talked to me.'

Lou needs to take a moment to compose herself and work out what to say next.

'Jake, you need to talk to the police. I am here for you darling and will do all I can to help. Sheila, please take Jake to the police station and talk this through. Call my solicitor to be there. Jakey, you have done the right thing darling, and we will get through this.'

Lou had dealt with the grief. The twins were buried, and she had been there, had her moment. She felt not relief but a sense of completion. She had done everything she could been there until the end. Yes, she wavered, yes, she drank too much and took too many pain killers for her ravaged body. In those few years she had done a lifetime's nursing work, alone. She didn't complain, she expressed her feelings, some listened, some turned away. Lou could hold her head high, she understood Jake's deep resentment of authority, the people present that night, particularly the SHO, and the shit just thrown at you. What she did want was for Jake was to build bridges with his dad. Lou's time in custody had given her time to reflect and she was ready to move on, but not with Ben. That was a previous life, a chapter that was now closed. Her love for the twins was unwavering but, Lou had moments in custody thinking; that's it, those worries about later life when she was incapable, or dead are now a distant memory. The twins have passed, just like the worry of what would happen to them, they died with their mum, carer and best fried at home. Tragically but peacefully. Lou had spent a lifetime worrying about the twins being farmed out to an authority-run institution with no life, no dignity, and no Lou. It was closure for Lou and now she needed to protect her son, Jake.

Jake lurches for his mum and gives the biggest closest, tightest cuddle he has had in years. The guards step forward but let it slide. Jake continues his sorry's to Lou who reassures him before he and Sheila head to the station.

Lou goes back to her cell, the emotional weight of being found guilty of a crime she is sure she didn't commit, the verdict of the trial lifted but with added fight now for her son. She knows how hard he has had it and can only think back to the Jake pre-twins.

He is still in there.

She goes into protection mode and starts to run through all the things she can do to help Jake now as he is not a criminal. His misguided love for his family and his hatred of authority led to committing the ultimate crime of compassion.

As Jake, Tina, and Sheila sit down, Raj joins them. After a short silence, Sheila prompts Jake to speak. Jake then spills out all the detail, explaining that the evidence he gave before was accurate up to the point where he met the group in the park and instead went to the house and murdered his brother and sister.

Raj and Tina arrest him, placing him in custody. Then had to go back to sort out Lou's conviction which was effectively null and void.

The detectives had sympathy for Jake's situation as he explained it was to relieve his mother's and the twins suffering, to go back to being a family. They just hadn't realised just how much it had affected him for all of those years, building up inside him, silently. It was obvious that Jake's dealings with the online world had taken him to dark places.

As Jake was led away, they had avoided a serious miscarriage of justice, sending the wrong person to jail for a crime they didn't commit. Jake's honesty through guilt had saved his mum and now he would have to face the jury but at least he had a clear conscience. The team now had the motive, evidence, and confession. Lou would be freed from prison to return to a life without the twins, without 24-hour caring duties. There would always be a hole in her heart after the death of her twins, but she would find a new way to live.

Epilogue

After the Storm there will be a Golden Sky

Lou was released from her incarceration, and she left to go back to an empty house. Deppy and Terry had readied the house for Lou's release, clearing all of the empty pots, pans, cups, and glasses. All of the medication had been taken as part of the investigation and Deppy Terry cleaned away all of the cardboard and crap around the house that had built up. Terry had prepared the twins empty bedrooms but left everything as it was for Lou to make the call on what happened next. The circumstances needed the ultimate respect and dignity with Lou now at the centre. The house was immaculate now, curtains open, windows open and Terry knew that Lou needed a different view and perspective and of her future. The bungalow needed to be filled with new smells, sounds and sights. How she remembered and honoured the twins life would be her own choice and her own path. Terry wanted to be on that path with her and was there for Lou 100%. Deppy was also giving everything for Lou and wanted to be a friend, support, and companion. Not just for the honeymoon period of grief, but for life. As Terry and Deppy tidy the twins room they look at the pictures and school art spread across the walls. The room is full of colour and life, a world away from the pain and the events of that fateful night. Terry turns on the fairy lights hanging around the headboards. He tucks the sheets in tightly. He had bought some fresh pillows – he wanted the rooms to look exactly as Lou would have left the room before bed every night in the early days. Although Lou had spiralled over lockdown, Terry remembers Lou wanted to keep a tight ship. The bedroom was the children's sanctuary and was a festival of lights and sounds to stimulate the children. As Terry and Deppy close the door, they hug and shed a tear. Terry adjusts the signs to a straight position on the door and they clear the lounge and Deppy unpacks the shopping supplies. They know Lou is being dropped off at 11am so they want everything beyond perfect.

The kitchen clock ticks to 11am, and they see a cab pull up on the pavement.

Terry clicks on Absolute 90's and Embrace is subtlety playing in the background with Come Back to What You Know. The house needs a distraction from silence. Lou looks painfully thin with her hair uncharacteristically short and no make-up. A world away from the glam Lou and the old her. Curtains are twitching as Lou walks slowly up to her closest friends in the world. Lou is hunched but there is no emotion, as her eyes raise up and lock with Terry's a very small smile appears on her face. Terry rubs his eyes smiles and the three of them hug. Terry can only say, 'Lou it's so good to see you'.

Lou nods and doesn't want to let go. As the embrace weakens, they separate, and Lou looks at the open door to the house. Terry and Deppy put their arms round Lou, and they walk up together, respectfully holding back so Lou can make the last few steps alone. She tentatively enters the fresh smelling house, bright and clean. It's like a first viewing to buy. She walks through every room, looking around each piece of furniture and each picture as if she's never seen it before. The personal care equipment is all gone, the nappy boxes and supplies have all gone. The place is unrecognisable . Terry and Deppy stay in the kitchen and give Lou time and space. As Lou walks round the house, she opens doors and starts opening windows to let the air and smells flush though the house. She completes the tour of the bungalow in the garden, closing her eyes and breathing in the air, feeling the breeze on her face and the sounds of the trees waving in the wind. Lou walks slowly back inside, leaving all the doors open. She stops and stares at the twins' bedroom door. Deppy and Terry know to leave this moment to Lou alone. Minutes pass as Lou just stares at the door, her mind is racing through the past and the moments she had with the twins. She thinks about Ben, her sister. The moments pre-kids, school, her friends -literally her whole life racing through in front of her. That night though is empty, it's been blanked, any memories have been erased and Lou only remembers the joy the twins brought her and those magical moment. Lou shuffles slowly to the door emblazoned with the name plaques – Edward and Holly. Lou feels the texture of the plaque and slowly opens the twins' bedroom door. It's cold but exactly as Lou remembers it in the good times. A shrine to the twins, the clocks have stopped. Lou scans the room, looking at every single painted picture, family photo, school photo. All of the twins' soft toys and games they had built up over time. There is so much to take in. Lou opens the drawers and puts her hands on the twins' clothes, folded neatly. The last thing she touches is the beds. The feed pumps and medical paraphernalia have gone. Lou stands at the foot of the beds surveying a scene of normality, taking comfort in this moment – this is what could have been.

Lou is thinking about the twins and Jake and Megan, knowing that she needs to look forward. She thinks of the deep love she now feels for Terry and her new circle, of Ben and Hetty as they continue their new life together. Rumours had got back to Lou about their relationship. Apparently, there is another side to Hetty, an insatiable lust that goes way beyond just Ben. There are rumours that Ben and Hetty are now firmly entrenched into the local swinging circuit and are known to travel up and down the A1 to one club or another and it's not for the music!

Lou feels no bitterness and smiles as she thinks about her old relationship with Ben and the deep deceit and abandonment of them both. She dodged a bullet. Lou has let it all go and feels nothing but love. Lou's time in jail had been spent reading, about Stoicism and Buddhism. A book that had changed her life was Man's Search for Meaning by Viktor E. Frankl. It put tragedy into perspective and Lou knew from that moment to cherish every day and look after her children left behind and bring them back together as a new family. She also knew that she wanted to start a new life with Terry and that he was her soulmate. She is in the bedroom for 20 minutes or more, trying to make sense of where she is now. It's a moment of clarity for Lou and her job now was to reconnect with Megan and be there unconditionally for Jake and build a new life.

Welcome to Holland

by Emily Perl Kingsley

I am often asked to describe the experience of raising a child with a disability - to try to help people who have not shared that unique experience to understand it, to imagine how it would feel. It's like this......

When you're going to have a baby, it's like planning a fabulous vacation trip - to Italy. You buy a bunch of guide books and make your wonderful plans. The Coliseum. The Michelangelo David. The gondolas in Venice. You may learn some handy phrases in Italian. It's all very exciting.

After months of eager anticipation, the day finally arrives. You pack your bags and off you go. Several hours later, the plane lands. The flight attendant comes in and says, "Welcome to Holland."

"Holland?!?" you say. "What do you mean Holland?? I signed up for Italy! I'm supposed to be in Italy. All my life I've dreamed of going to Italy."

But there's been a change in the flight plan. They've landed in Holland and there you must stay.

The important thing is that they haven't taken you to a horrible, disgusting, filthy place, full of pestilence, famine and disease. It's just a different place.

So you must go out and buy new guide books. And you must learn a whole new language. And you will meet a whole new group of people you would never have met.

It's just a different place. It's slower-paced than Italy, less flashy than Italy. But after you've been there for a while and you catch your breath, you look around.... and you begin to notice that Holland has windmills.... and Holland has tulips. Holland even has Rembrandts.

But everyone you know is busy coming and going from Italy... and they're all bragging about what a wonderful time they had there. And for the rest of your life, you will say "Yes, that's where I was supposed to go. That's what I had planned."

And the pain of that will never, ever, ever, ever go away... because the loss of that dream is a very very significant loss.

But... if you spend your life mourning the fact that you didn't get to Italy, you may never be free to enjoy the very special, the very lovely things ... about Holland.

* * *

Afterword

This book has been written for all of the parents dealing with lifetime disability. Whatever disability it may be, any sudden disability bestowed on a family or parents changes the course of life as you knew it.

Life is set up for normality and conformity. Daily life is still not set up for disability, particularly profound disability and the system is geared against the person who has been disabled or parents fighting daily for what they need for their child. Recognising the needs for parents, siblings, and society in general needs reform from years of chronic underfunding or wrongly placed funding.

Support is needed more than ever as society works its way through the disaster of social media, pandemic knock-on effects, self-serving short-term politicians, and a polarized society.

Siblings are often the forgotten ones when disability touches families. They need support, need to understand particularity as they wade through social media's ideal view of perfect and go through puberty, understanding what they are feeling and why.

Mental health support is sadly lacking throughout society and is massively underfunded and untargeted for families dealing with profound disabilities. On the outside siblings remain strong for the parents, they don't want to be a burden when parents are caring 24 hours a day, 7 days a week with very little support battling through the legal complexity.

Social care is broken and does barely enough to keep in touch with families. Health batters parents around, doing as little as they can get away with. Endless forms and assessments to get the basics and huge numbers of 'very well paid' staff to tell parents why they are not entitled to a decent wheelchair, bed, or mobility equipment or service. Disjointed services all working against each other and against the parents and their disabled children.

Throw education and the minefield you enter when a child gets to five years old, and the triad of incompetence is complete. Parents are then careering headlong into the service triad all battling against each other telling the parents they know what's best and they are all right. God help you if you try and fight for what you think is right.

Get to age 11, 16 and 18 and the triad gets even bigger, more complicated, and more sinister you are now at base camp with a mountain to climb.

For those without capacity, at 18 you lose all rights and the child you have been caring for from the womb. Your child is now at the hands of the state. Nobody tells you need to apply for an expensive court order. This has to change!

Silent struggle takes you on one journey that ultimately ends in tragedy. It shouldn't and doesn't have to be that way. Join the voices battling for change, battling for basic living provision, adequate equipment, fair care payments and adaptions and services based around the user and our expensive costs of living. Social care is massively under and wrongly resourced it needs a short- and long-term plan – it's not going away.

If you are fortunate to have normality throughout your life, be there for a family, child, adult, , friends, neighbour, or somebody you meet through your life or work that are not so fortunate. Actually, just saying 'hi', giving up your time or showing really interest makes such a difference to the everyday struggles.

For those families holding it together, that have held it together or are there for a family going through tough times. Keep going, enjoy every moment, smile, laugh, cry, listen but most of all never give in.

Keep talking and keep loving.

If you want to offer your support, join in the conversation, or want more help and advice go to:

www.silentstruggle.co.uk

Thank you

A Thought

To all the parents with children or adults with special needs don't suffer in silence. More importantly to all those parents of children and adults without special needs in their life please don't stare, don't walk, or look away, don't turn your back.

If you see a family or a carer out and about with a disabled child or young adult. A smile and a quick 'Hi, how are you doing today' could be a highlight or only interaction of their day.

A brief, friendly conversation means everything.

When parents are exposed to a world raising special needs children. Life throws up some unexpected challenges and test every aspect of your Stoicism. Spencer Bell

Printed in Great Britain
by Amazon